The Institute of Biol
Studies in Biology nu. 10

Population Dynamics

Second edition

Maurice E. Solomon

M.Sc., F.I.Biol.
Reader in Zoology and Head of Zoology Section,
Long Ashton Research Station,
University of Bristol

Edward Arnold

© Maurice E. Solomon 1976

First published 1969
by Edward Arnold (Publishers) Ltd.,
25 Hill Street, London W1X 8LL

Reprinted 1970, 1971 (twice), 1973
Second Edition 1976

Boards edition ISBN: 0 7131 2530 6
Paper edition ISBN: 0 7131 2531 4

Printed in Great Britain by
The Camelot Press Ltd., Southampton

General Preface to the Series

It is no longer possible for one textbook to cover the whole field of Biology and to remain sufficiently up-to-date. At the same time teachers and students at school, college or university need to keep abreast of recent trends and know where significant developments are taking place.

To meet the need for this progressive approach the Institute of Biology has for some years sponsored this series of booklets dealing with subjects specially selected by a panel of editors. The enthusiastic acceptance of the series by teachers and students at school, college and university shows the usefulness of the books in providing a clear and up-to-date coverage of topics, particularly in areas of research and changing views.

Among features of the series are the attention given to methods, the inclusion of a selected list of books for further reading and, wherever possible, suggestions for practical work.

Readers' comments will be welcomed by the authors or the Education Officer of the Institute.

1975

The Institute of Biology,
41 Queens Gate,
London, SW7 5HU

Preface to the second edition

How are the numbers of an animal or plant in particular places maintained in spite of losses, and limited in spite of reproduction? What are the causes of changes in abundance; how, if at all, is their influence related to the density of the population; how do they affect the proportion of young to mature individuals? Why are some populations dense, others sparse? How can the relationships in competition, predation, or population stability be expressed mathematically? Topics of this sort comprise the subject of population dynamics. Besides its theoretical interest, the subject is important for the control of pests, weeds and harmful animals, for the husbandry of domestic animals and crops, for the efficient use of fisheries, for the conservation of the flora and fauna of the countryside, and for the understanding (and control?) of changes in human populations.

For their criticisms of passages in the earlier edition I am grateful to many colleagues, including Professor J. L. Harper, Professor F. L. Milthorpe, Professor K. Bakker, Dr. F. Søgaard Andersen, Dr. H. F. van Emden, Dr. J. P. Dempster, Mr. E. N. Wright, Dr. M. C. Singer, Dr. R. Beaver and Dr. M. G. Solomon. I am indebted to the authors and institutions whose data or illustrations are acknowledged in various Figures and Tables, and thank them and their publishers for permission to use them.

Long Ashton, Bristol, 1975   M.E.S.

Contents

1 Characteristics of Populations

1.1 What is a population?

Although we all use the word 'population', or perhaps because of this, it is not easy to arrive at a strict and clear definition. Usually, a population is taken to be a group of organisms of one species (although one sometimes meets the phrase 'mixed-species population'). The group is usually separated in some degree from other groups of the same species, by geographical or topographical barriers (as on an island, or in a lake, or under a solitary stone), or by some boundary chosen by the investigator, who may, for instance, consider the codling moths in a particular orchard, or the frogs of a particular valley.

Some populations are clearly isolated and distinct, e.g. that of a species of lizard on a remote island. Some, through being for a long time completely cut off from other populations of their own kind, have evolved physical differences from the rest of the species: for example, the short-tailed vole has different forms, judged to be sub-species, on the islands of Eigg, Muck, Islay and Gigha. Many animals and plants have a patchy distribution, occurring in an irregular pattern of clumps and gaps. If the gaps are wide enough, the clumps can be treated as populations.

Of course, the clumps may be only temporarily separate. Each infested cabbage, and each cabbage field, may seem for a time to have its own population of cabbage aphis. But in the first place such colonies are set going by winged aphids borne on the wind and settling on the plants. Then, as each colony increases, it produces winged individuals which in turn take to the air as potential colonists. Not only are the local colonies temporary, their winged offspring mingle with aphids coming from other colonies.

Some animals tend to remain together in crowds during their wanderings, like schools of fish or swarms of locusts (Fig. 1–1). It is safe to assume that such groups, if they survive long enough, will intermingle with others of the same species.

If we know that a population in a particular area has been separate over a long period from others of the same species, it may seem appropriate to study it as a whole. But this may not be practicable. We may have to confine our attention to the part of it that we find in a particular valley or wood. We may call this part of it 'the population of' our selected place. But we must bear in mind that our boundary is not an absolute barrier, and try to measure the rate at which individuals pass out of or into the area of study. When we set about assessing the gains and losses to the

Fig. 1–1 (*above*) A small swarm of desert locusts (*Schistocerca gregaria*) photographed from the air in Kenya in 1953. Swarm moving towards left, and covering about 1 km². (Photographed by J. Sayer, reproduced by courtesy of Centre for Overseas Pest Control, London.)

(*below*) The cottony-cushion scale (*Icerya purchasi*) and a predatory ladybird *Rodolia koebelei*. The related *R. cardinalis* is the species which mainly controls the scale. (Courtesy Mr. F. Wilson, formerly of Sirex Biological Control Unit, Ascot, Berks.)

population by births and deaths, we have to count in, or allow for, these other gains and losses from immigration and emigration.

So, although we may have a clear mental picture of an ideal population, in its entirety and separateness, in practice we usually have to deal with a set of animals or plants that really forms only a section of such an ideal population, and which is not entirely separate from the larger population of the surrounding region. We shall be fortunate if it forms some sort of recognizable natural unit, and is separate most of the time from the surrounding members of the species. In any case, it is convenient, and usual, to refer to it as 'the population' under study.

1.2 Population of what?

To understand the biology of a population, we obviously need a knowledge of the biology of the individuals comprising it. Primarily, we should know the characteristics of the species concerned; we may then go on to enquire whether the members of the population under study differ individually or as a group from those in other populations of the same species.

Besides being aware of obvious features such as the size, shape, life-cycle, habits and behaviour of the organisms concerned, we may, according to the aims of our study, need to learn something of their physiology under the conditions in which the population is living, or their genetic make-up and the genetic pattern of the population as a whole. For various, often compelling practical reasons, many population studies take no account of such matters, and some are seriously weakened by this deficiency.

The great majority of animal populations, and some of plants, include two different types of individuals, male and female. Their numbers are not necessarily equal. Since it is only the females that reproduce, the ratio of females to males (sex ratio) is a matter of significance.

Another source of internal diversity is that most populations include a mixture of individuals of different ages. When, as in human populations, individuals of all ages are present simultaneously, it is useful to know the relative numbers in successive age intervals, i.e. the 'age distribution' or 'age composition' of the population. Table 1 shows the age distribution in a human population (for brevity, the smaller age groups of the original table have been amalgamated).

1.3 Numbers, dispersion and density

In spite of the above remarks on the importance of biological characteristics, our primary concern in the study of population dynamics is with numbers. We nearly always require to know how many individuals make up the population, or alternatively what the population density is (e.g. average number of individuals per square metre of meadow or per cubic metre of lake water). Sometimes, when we attach importance to the difference in weight between young and mature individuals, we may prefer to use units of biomass, i.e. weight of organisms per unit area or unit volume of habitat.

Table 1   Age distribution of the home population of the United Kingdom, 1961, in thousands. Based on Table 7 in *Annual Abstract of Statistics*. No. **104** (H.M.S.O.)

Age groups (years)	Nos. in groups	% in groups
0–9	8028	15.23
10–19	8003	15.18
20–29	6563	12.46
30–39	7083	13.44
40–49	7100	13.47
50–59	6958	13.20
60–69	5019	9.52
70–79	2937	5.57
80 & over	1017	1.93
Total:	52 708	100.00

If a population were spread uniformly throughout its habitat, a single figure for population density would apply throughout. But often the organisms are concentrated in certain parts, sparse or absent in others (uneven dispersion). Then the population density varies from place to place, so that the average density over the whole area may be an unrealistic guide to the effective density which the organisms experience.

The pattern of dispersion (or spatial distribution) of a population over the area it occupies is not usually regular. Even if the habitat is entirely uniform, which is seldom the case, and the members of a population are spread over it at random (i.e. as if the position of each one were determined by chance and were not influenced by the positions of its fellows), the pattern of dispersion will appear uneven in detail. Truly regular dispersion is to be seen in some plantations, such as that of the trees in an orchard, and is approached among certain animals or plants when they are of uniform size and closely packed together: sycamore aphids appear in a fairly regular pattern on a leaf by forming an aggregation, yet keeping each other 'at arm's length'. Most dispersion patterns, however, are not uniform, not even random, but show conspicuous clumps placed irregularly in a bare or sparsely occupied area. This may reflect irregularities of the habitat, reinforced by the reproduction of the organisms in the favourable spots; also, many animals tend to gather into groups, even on a uniform area. There are statistical methods for determining whether a dispersion pattern is more, or less, uniform than random.

The numbers in a population, or the density per unit area, are usually estimated by sampling, i.e. counting the numbers in small equal areas (etc.) selected at random. Clearly it is desirable to have a preliminary knowledge of a population's dispersion pattern when deciding on the size and number of the samples to be taken. On dispersion patterns and sampling, SOUTHWOOD (1966) or LEWIS and TAYLOR (1967) should be consulted.

2 Aspects of Population Dynamics

2.1 What is population dynamics?

If we say simply that population dynamics is the study of populations as functioning systems, this is true enough but it leaves far too much unexplained. This section will provide some further explanation.

In physical science, dynamics is the study of the behaviour of bodies under the action of forces that produce changes of motion in them. By analogy, the term population dynamics is applied to the study of changes in the numbers of organisms in populations and of the factors influencing these changes; also it includes the study of the rates of loss and replacement of individuals, and of any regulatory processes tending to keep the numbers steady, or at least to prevent excessive change.

The subject deals on the one hand with environmental influences upon populations, e.g. the effects of temperature and moisture, of the quantity of the food supply, of other species of organisms which compete for food or for other necessities, of natural enemies and of micro-organisms causing disease, and of various combinations of such factors. On the other hand it deals with the influence of members of the population upon each other, both favourable and adverse. The essential co-operative processes are those concerned with sexual reproduction and (in many species) the rearing of young. Also, members of a population may directly or indirectly protect each other to some extent from natural enemies, or against cold or other severe conditions, and they may modify the habitat to their joint advantage. Adverse influences may include competition for a limited supply of food, shelter or other requisites, mutual disturbance and fighting or even predation (cannibalism). External and internal influences may act in combination: e.g. adverse physical changes in the habitat may give rise to competition within the population for a few restricted refuges where conditions remain tolerable.

2.2 Questions in population dynamics

Although problems of population dynamics may occur to us in the course of spontaneous observations of nature, they arise much more often from our economic interests as hunters, fishermen, pastoralists, farmers or horticulturalists, and, nowadays, from our concern as conservationists. The following are a few examples of the questions that present themselves:

Why are some insects rather scarce and others abundant? What sorts of factors determine the difference?

What determines the abundance of rabbits, and how can their numbers be reduced?

Why is the shooting of wood-pigeons an ineffectual way of reducing their population in a region?

Why have red spider mite populations on apple trees often increased alarmingly when the trees have been sprayed to control codling moth?

Given a particular variety of wheat and type of soil and climate, what population density of plants will give the best yield per acre?

How much fishing will the North Sea herring populations withstand before being severely reduced, and what factors determine this?

At what level should whaling have been restricted to avoid putting various species in danger of extermination?

What is the best population density of sheep, or of cattle, on a given type of pasture, to secure the greatest annual yield of surplus animals that can be sold off?

How does the abundance of desert locusts depend on the weather, and how can we predict an outbreak?

Have the recent rapid increases in human populations been the result of increased birth rates or of reduced death rates, or both?

Some of these questions will be mentioned in later chapters, where the reader may find clues or even answers, and (more usefully) examples of ways in which such problems have been approached and solved.

2.3   Theory and reality

Answers to questions like those above may be suggested by close observation. However, natural conditions, or even those of agriculture or forestry, may be so complex that observations do no more than suggest hosts of possible explanations, or alternatively none at all. Experiments may be valuable as a means of putting proposed explanations to the test, but the results are often difficult to interpret unless many of the normally varying conditions have been stabilized. The practical investigation of population dynamics has been to a great extent concerned with ways of overcoming these difficulties.

Some biologists have preferred to study the dynamics of populations in the laboratory, where most of the variables can be kept constant. This is a flourishing branch of the subject, but two difficulties have arisen. The first is that we do not know how far we can apply the results of experiments under such artificially simplified conditions to the much more variable and complex situations in the field. This difficulty can in principle be overcome by gradually elaborating the laboratory experiments, making them larger and more complex, so as to bridge the gap between laboratory and field conditions. In practice this is a formidable undertaking, which has seldom been attempted. However, laboratory experiments have given us valuable insights into the dynamics of populations, and suggested ideas that may be tested in field experiments (by jumping the gap, rather than bridging it).

The second difficulty about laboratory experiments is that their apparent simplicity is often largely illusory. The more closely they are analysed, the more complex is the set of interactions revealed. This is a normal result of analytical investigation.

Other biologists, or sometimes the same ones, have undertaken theoretical studies in which simplicity is guaranteed, at least in the early stages, because the whole exercise is conducted with very simple imaginary models of populations and their environments. Usually the study proceeds in mathematical form. What the theorist is doing is to use mathematical logic to find out the implications of the simple set of circumstances he imagined to begin with. This is deductive thinking, in contrast to the inductive approach of the man who makes observations on real populations and tries to discover explanations of the events he sees, by finding out what other events lead up to them.

There is no doubt that the theoretician has a much less laborious task than the practical investigator. His theory readily branches out in various directions, it can be systematically elaborated, it reveals surprising relationships that were not predictable offhand. He does, of course, need at least a modest command of algebra. But a crucial difficulty, regarded by some biologists as rendering theoretical studies largely valueless, is that the 'field' in which he operates is even more remote from reality out-of-doors than are laboratory experiments, and therefore we do not know to what extent his discoveries and conclusions apply in actuality. There is a good deal of truth in this: the initial assumptions which set the stage for a theoretical study need to be scrutinized very closely, and their validity tested against known facts or against new observations or experiments. On the other hand, theoretical studies have at the least provided stimuli of the first importance for the development of population dynamics. They have been a most valuable source of ideas to be tested in practice, and have provided starting points for a good deal of productive research.

Recent thinking favours the development of theoretical models and practical studies step by step together (HOLLING, 1963, 1964). Ideally, the procedure should be somewhat as follows. First, a simple model is written down, the assumptions and relationships being based as far as possible on knowledge of particular populations. Then the assumptions and relationships of the model are tested in field studies, and modified if necessary. Practical work also supplies numerical values for various symbols (terms) in the algebraic model. The next step is to develop the model mathematically, to derive some of its implications. These in turn can be tested in practical work.

This sort of development produces increasingly complex models. Fortunately modern computers can often deal with the mathematics involved, especially if the model has been constructed with computer programming in mind.

2.4 The place of population dynamics in ecology

'Subjects' are convenient subdivisions of knowledge and of areas of study, rather than distinct 'islands'. They overlap the boundaries with related subjects. This is notably true of ecology itself, and of the subdivisions of ecology. A distinction is commonly made between the study (1) of individuals, (2) of populations and (3) of communities.

Under (1) we class investigations of the effects upon individuals of temperature, moisture and other physical factors, of other organisms, of food supply, and so on. Such studies are often regarded as ecological (but overlapping, at least, with other subjects such as physiology and behaviour). Whilst they may provide valuable support for population dynamics, they are not a part of this subject.

But if we study the effects of temperature, food supply, etc., upon populations, as influencing their performance, distribution and abundance, we are concerned with population dynamics. If we investigate the interactions within or between populations, or their rates of increase or decline, we are again dealing with population dynamics.

At the third level of organization we have community ecology. This deals with the relations between the populations of plants and animals living together in the same place (habitat). It is concerned with the structure of communities—the trees, shrubs and herbs, herbivorous and carnivorous animals, the micro-organisms that break down dead organic materials, and so on, the number of different species in each category, and their relations to each other as producers (green plants) or as consumers of plant or animal material. A series of organisms, each of which feeds on the preceding organisms, is called a food-chain, and the flow of material through the series can be studied quantitatively, as can the flow of energy (cf. PHILLIPSON, 1966). Competition, predation and parasitism between the populations of a community are a part of this subject, as is the succession that occurs when some species are replaced by others in, for example, the development of a community from grassland to woodland. The physical environment is again important in this connection. The complex of plants, animals and physical environment is called an ecosystem, envisaged as an integrated system of interacting elements.

A related subject is zoogeography, concerned with the distribution of species and communities on a wider, often world-wide, scale. Zoogeographers are concerned with finding what geographic, climatic or other factors determine the presence or absence of species or communities in the various regions of the world, with the role of oceans or mountain ranges as barriers to dispersal, with the effects of the drifting of the continents in past ages, and with the influence of competition or natural enemies in excluding particular species (or higher groups, e.g. marsupials) from certain regions.

3 The Functioning of Populations: Gains and Losses

3.1 The power of increase

Reproduction is characteristic of all species of organisms. As pointed out long ago by Malthus, it is a multiplicative process. Reproductive adults normally replace themselves by a greater number of offspring. Under favourable conditions, this increase more than compensates for the deaths that commonly occur during juvenile development, and there is a net rate of multiplication.

If for a moment we ignore mortality and other losses, and consider the reproductive rate of surviving adults, this is often impressive. Many insects lay hundreds of eggs, many frogs and toads lay thousands, and some fishes, such as the cod, produce millions. Even allowing for mortality, very high net rates of multiplication may be observed: when reared under highly favourable conditions in the laboratory, the flour or grain mite can increase seven-fold in a week.

If conditions remained favourable for continued multiplication, the numbers reached would soon be enormous. One hundred grain mites would become 700 in one week, 4900 in 2 weeks, 34 300 in 3 weeks, and over 28 thousand million in 10 weeks. The last figure is unrealistic, because overcrowding would spoil the conditions for rapid increase before any such level was approached; but it illustrates the tendency towards population explosion inherent in the reproductive process. Even a doubling of numbers per year is equivalent to 1000-fold increase in 10 years, or 10-million-fold in 20 years.

In the 1920s, the American biologist R. N. Chapman proposed to call the maximum rate of increase, of which an organism was capable under the most favourable conditions, its 'biotic potential' (see CHAPMAN, 1931). This was imagined to be opposed and reduced under less favourable conditions by 'environmental resistance'. Environmental resistance included the causes of mortality, and conditions (such as crowding, food shortage, cold, etc.) which reduced the rate of reproduction. If Chapman had been more successful in the logical development of this electrical analogy, and had gone on to use real circuits to imitate population dynamics, he would have been the inventor of the analogue computer. In the event, the ideas of biotic potential and environmental resistance remained too vague to be of much practical value. Nevertheless, interest in the rates of increase that populations are capable of under various conditions has continued. Obviously, the rate at which a pest or a useful animal can increase is something which concerns the economic biologist.

3.2 Mortality

In population biology, 'mortality' strictly means the rate of death, e.g.
20 per cent dying per year (and 'natality' is the corresponding term for the
birth rate); but it is often employed simply as a synonym of death, or
deaths, and I follow the perhaps reprehensible custom of using it in both
senses.

Alongside reproduction, mortality is the twin starting point for most
studies of population dynamics. Broadly (allowing for fluctuations and
dispersal) these two phenomena offset each other. In this context,
'mortality' is shorthand for 'pre-reproductive mortality'. It is not just
deaths, but early deaths, which more or less counterbalance the effect of
reproduction in most animal populations.

The pre-reproductive death rate required to hold a population in
check depends of course on its powers of reproduction. If an animal has
equal numbers of males and females, and each female produces on
average 20 young, the mortality required to prevent an increase in
numbers is 90 per cent; if 200 young, then 99 per cent mortality; if 2000
young, 99.9 per cent mortality.

The mortality may be measured and expressed in various ways, for
example as numbers dying per week or per generation, as percentage of
the whole population per year, or as percentages of age-groups within the
population per month, and so on. Demographers (students of human
populations) deal in survival rates rather than mortality. Their procedure
is to compose a table, starting with a convenient number of new-born
individuals and showing how many of these would survive in successive
intervals through the whole life span. This display of the 'age-specific'
survival rate is commonly called a 'life table'. For human populations,
such data (Table 2) are required for national statistics and by life
insurance companies who wish to estimate their risks as precisely as
possible. Corresponding tables are sometimes drawn up for populations
of animals. Table 3 is for the spruce budworm in an area of Eastern
Canada. The caterpillars of this moth feed on the leaves of conifers. The
table illustrates features common to many life tables for animals. The life
cycle is divided into a relatively small number of intervals, and these
intervals are of unequal length, corresponding to recognizable life history
stages. This is because of the laboriousness of estimating the numbers in
wild populations by sampling, and the difficulty of determining the
precise age of individuals. It is also convenient, as in Table 3, to begin
with the average number of eggs laid per female—200 in this instance.
This is an averaged, or mean, life table based on 10 years' observations. It
gives a simplified, tidied-up version of the spruce budworm's reproduction, mortality and dispersal; in reality, the values, and consequently
the abundance of the budworm, vary considerably from year to year and
from place to place.

Table 2   Life table for U.K., 1964–66. From *Annual Abstract of Statistics*. No. **104** (H.M.S.O.).The lx column shows the numbers surviving at the beginning of each successive 5-year age interval, starting with 10 000 new-born infants. Column èx shows the average expectation of life at these ages

Age X	Males		Females	
	lx	èx	lx	èx
0	10 000	68.2	10 000	74.5
5	9 742	65.1	9798	71.0
10	9719	60.2	9783	66.1
15	9699	55.4	9770	61.2
20	9651	50.6	9751	56.3
25	9599	45.9	9728	51.4
30	9551	41.1	9699	46.6
35	9494	36.3	9659	41.8
40	9405	31.6	9595	37.0
45	9258	27.1	9489	32.4
50	9013	22.8	9324	27.9
55	8595	18.8	9076	23.6
60	7915	15.2	8713	19.5
65	6819	12.1	8157	15.7
70	5513	9.4	7306	12.2
75	3935	7.2	6049	9.2
80	2345	5.4	4385	6.8
85	1051	4.0	2504	5.0

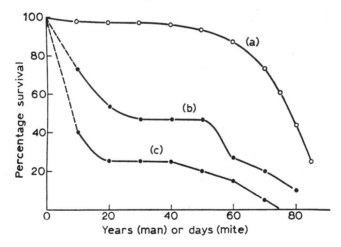

Fig. 3–1   Survivorship curves for females of man (curve (a), from Table 2) and of a predatory mite (*Cheyletus eruditus*) reared in the laboratory at 20°C, 65 per cent relative humidity (b) and at 25°C, 85 per cent R.H. (c).

Table 3   Abbreviated 'mean' life table for spruce budworm at Green River, New Brunswick, Canada (Modified from MORRIS, 1957)

Age interval (x)	No. alive at beginning of x (lx)	Factors responsible for mortality	No. dying during x (dx)	dx as % of lx (100 qx)
Egg	200	Parasites	10	5
		Other	20	10
		Total	30	15
Early larva	170	Dispersal	136	80
Later larva	34	Parasites	13.6	40
		Disease	6.8	20
		Other	10.2	30
		Total	30.6	90
Pupa	3.4	Parasites	0.3+	10
		Other	0.5+	15
		Total	0.9	25
Moth	2.5	Miscellaneous	0.5	20

Generation survival 2 (1 per cent)
Generation mortality 198 (99 per cent)
Sex ratio taken as 1 : 1 (equal numbers males and females)

In Fig. 3–1, the values for survival of females in Table 2 have been used to construct a 'survivorship curve' (a). Curves (b) and (c) in the same figure are based on corresponding data for a mite. The difference in shape is an aspect of the contrast between (a) a population with a relatively low reproductive rate, but high survival rate until towards the end of the life span, and (b and c) a population with very high reproductive rate but with rather heavy mortality in the early stages of the life span. Many examples of both types are known.

3.3   Dispersal

Many animals can fly, run or drift from their original habitat, and there is often a particular stage in the life cycle when they tend to do this. Sometimes the proportion that is lost by dispersal depends on the population density. More may be lost by dispersal than by death. In any case, dispersal losses are equivalent to mortality in the balance sheet of population numbers. Of course, dispersal may add individuals to the population as well as taking them away; these two processes are often referred to as immigration and emigration, although the word migration (without prefix) is more often applied to concerted directional movements like the flight of various birds southwards from northerly latitudes as winter approaches.

3.4   Assessing rates of increase

So long as the balance of gains and losses is positive, a population will be increasing. The practical work required in estimating the rate of increase is seldom easy; the degree of difficulty depends on the circumstances and on the level of accuracy required. Basically, the practical task is to estimate the numbers at intervals, usually by taking samples and counting the numbers in each. Complete censuses of populations are sometimes possible with the larger animals or plants, or with laboratory cultures. Fig. 3–2a is the graph of a series of estimates, each made on a different culture of mites; a number of similar cultures had been set up simultaneously in the same way, kept under the same conditions, and taken out after various periods for estimation of the numbers of mites.

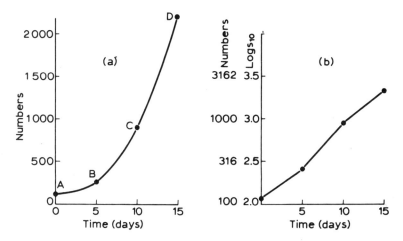

Fig. 3–2   (a) Observed increase of the mite *Acarus siro* in grain at 25°C, 80 per cent relative humidity. (b) The same data on a logarithmic scale of numbers.

The calculation of the rate of increase from such estimates may be done simply enough. The net rate of multiplication (i.e. the geometric rate of increase) over any unit period is the number at the end of the period divided by the number at the beginning. In the three successive 5-day periods in Fig. 3–2a, the rates of increase are:

$$B/A = 258/118 = 2.19 \text{ in } 5 \text{ days}$$
$$C/B = 900/258 = 3.49 \text{ in } 5 \text{ days}$$
$$D/C = 2190/900 = 2.43 \text{ in } 5 \text{ days}$$

If we knew only A and D, and wished to calculate the mean rate of increase per 5-day period, we could call this mean rate x, and write:

$$D = Ax^3, \text{ whence } x = (D/A)^{1/3} = 2.65$$

This is the same as a compound interest calculation, in which x would be the (constant) rate of interest.

A characteristic of steady geometric increase is that it generates a straight line slope when numbers are graphed on a logarithmic scale. The above population estimates are plotted on a logarithmic scale in Fig. 3–2b; the fact that the points are not precisely in line expresses the same deviations from a steady rate of increase as were shown by the above calculations. One might expect such variation to arise from uncontrolled differences between cultures, but in the present instance they also reflect real changes in the rate of increase. The rates of increase could be assessed graphically, by measuring the slopes of the lines joining the points in Fig. 3–2b. Rates of decrease could be assessed from a down-sloping line in a corresponding way.

It often happens that, instead of observing the increase of a population, we have data from rearing experiments. These may tell us how long, under a particular set of conditions, the animal takes to develop from the egg or new-born young to the reproductive stage, how many eggs or young are produced per female, and at what times in her life. If the reproductive period is much shorter than the developmental period, a simple calculation gives an approximate value for the rate of increase. Suppose, for example, an insect takes 3 months to develop to a short-lived adult stage, suffering 50 per cent mortality in the process, and laying, on average, 100 eggs between the 95th and 100th day of the female's life, with the highest number laid on the 97th day. We shall not be distorting the facts too much if we imagine all the eggs to be laid on the 97th day. Then if the sex-ratio is 1:1, the daily rate of multiplication, x, can be derived as follows:

Start with 4 eggs, 2 male and 2 female.
After 97 days, one male and one female survive, and the female lays 100 eggs. Thus 4 eggs give rise to 100 eggs in 97 days.
Therefore $4x^{97} = 100$, or $x^{97} = 25$, or $97 \log x = \log 25$,
    whence x (the daily rate of multiplication) $= 1.034$.
The weekly rate of multiplication would be $x^7 = 1.261$.

Values derived in this way might be applicable to, say, a mixed-age population of a stored-food pest under constant, uncrowded coditions in the laboratory. (If we started with adults only, we should have a much higher rate of increase whilst they were reproducing, then no further increase until the offspring had grown to the adult stage. If we started with eggs, there would be no increase while the young developed, then a burst of multiplication by the adults, then another pause. These periodic waves of increase would gradually spread into a continuous process as the age composition of the population became more mixed.)

But with a field population in a temperate climate, the rate of increase would vary with the weather, food supply, etc. Also, the population might well be all of about the same age, and have only one or two generations in the warmer part of the year, remaining inactive over the winter. In such cases we should be interested chiefly in the rate of increase per generation, and in the influence of the current weather and other varying conditions upon this rate.

If an animal has an extended reproductive period, the above simple method of calculation is inapplicable. There is a relatively elaborate method of calculating the so-called 'finite rate of increase' (λ), which is the mulitiplication rate of a freely increasing population in which the proportion of individuals of various ages has settled down to a certain 'stable age distribution', characteristic of the population in the set of conditions concerned. The natural logarithm of λ is called the 'innate capacity for increase' (r). This represents the infinitesimal rate of increase in the differential equation $dN/dt = rN$, where N is the number of animals in the population. If N_t and N_{t+1} represent the numbers before and after a unit time interval, the relationship between λ and r can be expressed as:

$$N_{t+1}/N_t = e^r = \lambda, \text{ or } r = \log_e \lambda$$
($e = 2.718 \ldots$, the base of natural or Napierian logarithms).

The method of calculating r from rearing data is described in the books by ANDREWARTHA and BIRCH (1954) and SOUTHWOOD (1966).

Another way of calculating the increase of a population, starting with a knowledge of the life cycle and the age distribution, is provided by matrix algebra. This method, and its application to examples in which a part of the population is periodically harvested, is explained by WILLIAMSON (1967).

3.5   Population growth curves

We have remarked that population increase cannot continue indefinitely. As the habitat becomes crowded, or as the exploitation of some essential requisite becomes more nearly complete, the rate of increase must diminish until the numbers reach a saturation point at which no further increase is possible. The overall curve representing increase from low numbers to saturation point is S-shaped (sigmoid) when a straightforward arithmetic scale of numbers is used (cf. Fig. 3–3).

A well-known model of such population growth is the logistic or

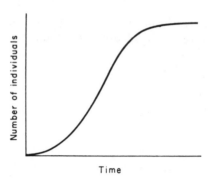

Fig. 3-3   A logistic curve of population growth.

Verhulst–Pearl curve. This is a highly simplified model, based on the following assumptions: All the animals are effectively identical—at any particular time, all are equally likely to reproduce, and all equally likely to die; the rate of increase at any time depends only on the numbers present; when expressed in a certain way, the rate of increase is linearly proportional to the degree of unsaturation of the habitat, or to the difference between the saturation density and the density at the time. (Here we take density and numbers to be alternative ways of expressing the size of the population. Another way is to take biomass, the combined weight of all the individuals present.) Finally, it is assumed that the temperature and other environmental conditions are constant. From these assumptions the following equation can be derived:

$$\frac{dN}{dt} = rN\frac{(K-N)}{K}$$

where dN/dt is the instantaneous net rate of addition to the population, r is the innate capacity for increase (cf. page 17), N is the number of individuals present, and K is the number the habitat can hold at saturation (so that $\frac{(K-N)}{K}$ represents the degree of unsaturation of the habitat).

A more usual equivalent of this equation is:

$$N = \frac{K}{1 + e^{a-bt}}$$

where a and b are constants related to the steepness and height of the curve, and t is the time (on the scale along the x axis).

The logistic equation has been very widely used in the interpretation of population growth curves. It does not follow that the assumptions it is based on hold true in these cases: very often it is clear that they cannot possibly apply. For an analysis that is biologically realistic, other models of sigmoid curves may have to be developed, on the basis of assumptions appropriate to the case.

4 The Functioning of Populations: Fluctuation and Regulation

4.1 Fluctuations in abundance

In the previous chapter we remarked the great power of increase inherent in many animals; on the other hand, disaster may strike suddenly and take a high proportion of the population. In consequence, many populations are subject to considerable fluctuations in numbers. Some fluctuate slowly, some rapidly, some strikingly and continually, others rather little, or at long intervals.

The causes of population fluctuation are many. Notably, with insects, they include seasonal and other changes in the weather, but also changes in food supply, and the attacks of natural enemies including the micro-organisms causing disease. Sometimes one particular factor can be identified as the chief cause of fluctuation in a population, and is referred to as the 'key factor'. Sometimes we can distinguish between immediate and underlying causes of fluctuation. For example, weather may affect the numbers of aphids directly, by killing some of them, or it may affect them indirectly by altering the condition of the plants they feed upon.

A special type of fluctuation is seen in all animals (and plants) that have a reproductive period restricted to a particular season. There is then a periodic rapid increase by production of young, followed by a more gradual decline as death or dispersal reduces the numbers. Fig. 4–1 illustrates such a case.

Usually we are more concerned with the less regular fluctuations in numbers caused by environmental factors. In a seasonally reproducing population like that in Fig. 4–1, such fluctuations may be detected by comparing the numbers at one particular stage of development in successive years (dashed line): here, the range of fluctuation in numbers of adult grasshoppers from year to year is approximately from 1000 to 3500. Figure 4–2 shows the same phenomenon (inter-generation fluctuation) in a population of the pine beauty moth, as determined by estimating the density of the population of pupae in the ground at a site in Germany. On the arithmetic scale (solid line) we see a decline ending about 1925, and an outbreak and decline around 1931; at other times the numbers were relatively low and seem rather steady. This steadiness is only apparent, as is seen when the numbers are plotted on a logarithmic scale (dashed line). Because the logarithmic scale clearly displays fluctuations at low density, and keeps the great increases to a reasonable height on the graph, and for other reasons, it is widely used for plotting population figures, as here and in Fig. 4–1.

Fig. 4–1 Annual population cycle of the grasshopper *Chorthippus brunneus* on a site in Berkshire. O Adults, ● eggs, + nymphs. The dashed line shows fluctuations in numbers of adults in successive generations. (Based on RICHARDS, O. W. and WALOFF, N. (1954), *Studies on the Biology and Population Dynamics of British Grasshoppers*, Bulletin **17**, Anti-Locust Research Centre, London.)

Fig. 4–2 Counts of pupae of pine beauty, a noctuid moth whose larvae attack the needles of Scots firs, at Neuendorf in Germany. Dashed line shows numbers on logarithmic scale. (Data of SCHWERDTFEGER, F. (1942). *Z. angew. Entom.*, **28**, 254–303.)

If we set out to study and interpret the changes in abundance of a population from generation to generation, an early step is to try to identify the 'key factor', which, as mentioned above, is the one responsible for the greatest proportion of the fluctuation. Here, it is the amount of change we are concerned with. We may find, for example, that differences in temperature account for more of the difference in abundance from generation to generation than does any other factor. In that case, temperature is the key factor. Other factors may cause a higher mortality, but so long as their effect is less variable from generation to generation than the effect of temperature, the latter remains the key factor. Such information is useful, not only as a step towards the analysis of the dynamics of the population, but also as a means of forecasting the trend of abundance (assuming there is a time lag in the appearance of some of the effects of temperature upon the population). Convenient explanations of key factor analysis, and of the methods used, are given by VARLEY, GRADWELL, and HASSELL (1973) and SOUTHWOOD (1966).

Fluctuation is characteristically irregular. When a regular pattern appears, we often prefer to call it a cycle. The annual cycle of reproduction and subsequent decline (Fig. 4–1) is a case in point.

4.2   Regulation and density-dependent processes

We have remarked that populations may fluctuate irregularly in response to changes in weather or under the influence of other environmental factors. We may be tempted to think that whether they increase or decrease, and by how much, is a matter of chance, like the weather from week to week. But if this were the whole story, there would be nothing to prevent the fluctuations gradually or rapidly making the population more abundant, or less abundant; there would be nothing to prevent the 'ups and downs' drifting preponderantly in one direction or the other, until the population either died out or entirely overran its environment. Most populations that have been observed do not do this; although they change in abundance from generation to generation, over a period they tend to preserve a characteristic level of abundance, so that we can say a species is 'common' or 'rare' or 'very abundant' in a particular habitat, and if there are striking changes at times, so long as the habitat retains its essential features the animals generally return fairly soon to their characteristic abundance or scarcity (see Figs. 4–1, 4–2.)

Another consideration is the probability, and in many cases the observed fact, that, as abundance increases, there is a progressive building up of resistance; at least there appear drastic checks to further increase when the numbers rise above a certain level. For example, at high densities there may be a shortage of food, or the animals may continually disturb each other, or one of their natural enemies may exploit the large numbers better than it did the smaller ones. In one way or another, at a certain stage the further increase of the population is first hindered and then prevented, and finally the numbers may be forced down again (for example, if the food supply has been over-taxed, there may be a period of famine). Increasing penalties against rising density are the essential feature of the idea of 'regulation'.

If the increase of a population is to be limited in this way, there must be at least one adverse influence that comes into play more strongly when the numbers rise, and ultimately stops further increase. When the numbers decline again (through a persistence of the adverse influence that has stopped increase, or through an unfavourable change in some other factor, such as the weather), the adverse factor that was called into play by the rise in abundance often becomes less effective (if it does not do so, the population may be exterminated). Factors which operate in this way, becoming more effective at high population density, and less effective at low density, are called 'density-dependent'. There may be several such factors operating at different times or places, or at different levels of abundance, or all together, contributing to the regulation of population.

Sometimes the inspection of a series of population counts will yield evidence of regulation. It may enable us to answer the questions: Does the proportional rate of increase decline when, or where, the numbers are high? Does the population decrease more often, and perhaps more rapidly, when numbers are high than when they are low? Is the rate of increase proportionately greater when numbers are low? Does the population increase more rapidly and/or more often when numbers are low?

In the field, even if we think we can detect such tendencies, there will be many exceptions to the general trend. There will also be false evidence, e.g. when the weather changes adversely at a time when numbers are high and produces effects which may be only partly, if at all, a response to high density. Therefore we require a long series of observations so that the regulatory trends may appear clearly through the non-regulatory fluctuations. We shall need statistical tests to show whether or not the apparent density-related trends have a significant probability of having arisen by chance.

Regulation, as we remarked, is a result of the action of density-dependent factors. (We shall see shortly that this way of putting the matter is somewhat inadequate, but it will serve for the present.) How can we determine whether or not a particular factor is acting in a density-dependent way? The straightforward approach to this is to assess its adverse effect at different levels of population density or abundance. As an example we may take the case illustrated in Fig. 4–3. The animals concerned are the caterpillars of the winter moth; they feed on oak leaves and incidentally swallow the eggs of a parasitic fly which lays them mostly where the foliage has been damaged. In a wood near Oxford, the entomologists Varley and Gradwell estimated the population density of the caterpillars on each of five oak trees, by collecting samples. They counted the proportion that contained parasites (which would ultimately kill them). The graph shows that where the caterpillars were more abundant, a higher proportion of them were parasitized, i.e. the parasite was acting as a density-dependent factor.

Before leaving this example, we may use it to illustrate some other notable features of density-dependent factors:

(1) It is not enough for the adverse effect to increase as population density increases: there must be a *proportional* increase in the effect. Fig. 4–3 shows that roughly 10 per cent were parasitized when the population density was 50, and about 19 per cent when the density was 150. This is of course a proportional increase in the incidence of parasitism. Considering the animals per unit space, at the lower density there were 50, of which 5 were parasitized, and at the higher density there were 150 of which 28 or 29 were parasitized. Suppose only 10 had been parasitized at the higher density; although this would still have been twice as many as at the lower density, there would not have been a proportional increase in parasitism—the percentage would have been only 6.6 per cent; there would have been no tendency for parasitism to increase faster than the population, so as to overtake it and, at a certain level, prevent its further increase.

(2) Fig. 4–3 shows us that the percentage parasitism continued to rise, as population density increased, up to about 22 per cent at the highest observed density (about 175). It does not tell us how much further it would have risen if there had been even higher population densities. We must not assume that it would necessarily have gone on rising as shown in Fig. 4–3 to reach, at some high density of winter moth caterpillars, a high value such as 80 or 90 per cent parasitization. It might well have been that there were not enough parasites, or not enough of their eggs, to accomplish this.

(3) It follows from the above that we cannot tell, from the information in Fig. 4–3, whether or not the parasite was effectively regulating the abundance of the winter moth, i.e. preventing its increase beyond a certain density. It was apparently making a contribution towards this, but it may have been necessary for other factors to finish the job. Thus, while regulation cannot be achieved without one or more density-dependent factors, it does not follow that every density-dependent factor is exercising regulation.

The adverse influence concerned in Fig. 4–3 is a form of mortality (parasitized individuals die before being able to reproduce). Fig. 4–4 illustrates another example in which mortality increases as density rises. This relationship is clearly seen in laboratory experiments, like the one illustrated, in which numbers of animals are confined in a small space with a limited food supply. The more crowded they are, and the smaller the share of food per individual, the higher the proportion that dies before maturity. Other consequences of such conditions may be smaller individuals and a reduced rate of reproduction. (A similar example is to be seen in Fig. 4–9.) In the study on which Fig. 4–4 is based, the experimenter did not determine the cause of the density-dependent effect—whether, for example, it was food-shortage or mutual disturbance. In the following examples also (Figs. 4–5 and 4–6), the only cause specified is increased population density, so that density-dependent factors are not distinguished. Very often in ecological work, the stage illustrated is reached first, and the more searching analysis of causes is attempted later.

Unlike the earlier examples, in which the adverse effect of raised density was increased mortality, the effect shown in Fig. 4–5 has to do with dispersal. Crowding increases the production of winged forms, which subsequently leave the plants.

The effect illustrated in Fig. 4–6 is of yet another kind: it takes the form of a reduction in the numbers of young birds successfully reared by each pair when the breeding population is high. If we were to make a graph of this *reduction*, it would be similar in orientation to the other examples of density-dependence we have seen. But the graph shows *performance*, which declines as density rises, so the trend of the points in Fig. 4–6 is

Fig. 4–3   Percentage parasitism of winter moth caterpillars by the parasitic fly *Cyzenis albicans* on 5 oak trees in Wytham Wood, nr. Oxford, 1957. (HASSELL, M. P. (1966). *J. Anim. Ecol.*, **35**, 65–75.)

Fig. 4–4   Mortality of caterpillars of the Indian-meal moth confined on 20 g of food. (Data of SNYMAN, A. (1949). *J. Entom. Soc. S. Afr.*, **12**, 137–71.)

Fig. 4–5   Percentage of winged nymphs (4th instar) of the cabbage aphid in relation to numbers on plants. At Canberra, Australia. (After CLARK, GEIER, HUGHES and MORRIS, 1967; courtesy of Methuen & Co. Ltd.)

Fig. 4–6   Breeding success of great tit in Marley Wood, nr. Oxford, in relation to number of breeding pairs present, 1947 to 1963. (After LACK, 1966; courtesy of The Clarendon Press.)

downwards, instead of upwards as in Figs. 4–3 to 4–5. The effects of density become more severe as density rises, but performance, as reduced by these density effects, declines. Further examples of density-dependence expressed in this way may be seen in later sections (Figs. 4–10, 6–1b, 6–2).

4.3   Factors, processes and density-relationships

When we refer to a 'factor', we are using a convenient mental device to separate for special attention a particular aspect of the whole complex presented by a population in its environment. Any part or aspect of this complex can be regarded as a factor influencing the population, as, for example, predators, temperature, or mutual disturbance. The working of any influence upon the population is best referred to as a 'process': predators are a factor; predation, although we may refer to it as a factor, is more appropriately called a process. An aspect of the processes affecting populations is their density-relationship—whether, for example, they are intensified at high densities. A process that is affected in this or in some other way by the density of the population is 'density-related'.

The action of a density-dependent factor can be compared with that of the governor on an engine—a device which restricts the supply of liquid or fuel as the engine runs faster, and increases the supply as the speed falls. In cybernetics, such action is called 'negative feed-back'. In populations, we do not find the precision and repeatability that engineers demand, but the general idea is common to both fields.

Envisaging such simple and direct density-dependent action by a single factor, we may say that such a factor must be responsive to changes in the density of the population it acts upon. It must itself be influenced by this population density, just as the governor must be influenced by the speed of the engine if it is to regulate it. Processes generated by the population itself (e.g. competition for something, mutual disturbance) are inevitably and automatically density-dependent.

4.4   Non-regulatory processes

Having recognized the special features of those processes tending to bring about regulation, i.e. of density-dependent processes, we may consider the characteristics of some other sorts. Factors (or processes) that affect a population in a way which is unrelated to its density are called 'density-independent'. For example, if a proportion of the insects and spiders in a pasture are killed by the trampling of cattle, it is probable that the percentage affected will not depend upon whether these arthropods are sparse or abundant. (The percentage killed will of course depend on the population density of the *cattle*, and the *numbers* killed will depend on the population density of the arthropods as well as on that of the cattle, but neither of these relationships is relevant to the question of whether the cattle are a density-dependent factor for the arthropods.) It is not that a density-independent factor usually remains constant in its proportional effect while the density varies; it is much more likely to vary a good deal from time to time or from place to place: but so long as the variations in its influence are not significantly correlated with the variation in density, it remains density-independent. An example is illustrated in Fig. 4–7.

Fig. 4–7   A density-independent relationship: the length of a generation of the ciliate protozoan *Woodruffia metabolica* and its population density in a laboratory culture. (SALT, G. W. (1967). *Ecol. Monogr.*, **37**, 113–44.)

The effects of weather are often assumed to be density-independent, and no doubt this is very frequently true for all practical purposes. But, as we have already noted, the effects of particular factors are commonly influenced by the effects of others. The weather itself is not influenced by population density, but its effect may be. For example, the animals may have been abundant enough to eat down the vegetation which would otherwise have provided shelter against rain or drought, so that few now survive the downpour or the dry conditions. If they had been less numerous, their shelter might have been preserved. Even if the animals have not damaged their habitat in this way, if there are far more of them than the sheltering sites can accommodate, the surplus will either move away or (as we assume here) will be killed. The proportion that is killed by the severe weather will depend on the abundance of the animals. Does this mean that the effect of the weather is density-dependent? Only if we ignore the part played by the limited supply of shelter. An inadequate supply of anything that is needed by the animals has density-dependent consequences: the more animals there are, the higher the proportion that must go short, or the smaller is the share of each member of the population. Some ecologists would say that the density-dependent effect is provided by competition for the limited supply (competition being automatically density-dependent). Perhaps the most satisfactory statement of the matter is that weather, the capacity of the shelters, and the numbers of the animals jointly bring into play a density-dependent process.

Besides density-independent processes, there is another type whose effect is non-regulatory. This is the opposite of density-dependent, inasmuch as the adverse influence is proportionately *smaller* when numbers are higher than when numbers are low. For example, predators or insect parasites often increase their rate of attack when the numbers of their prey increase, but not in proportion—the percentage attacked is less than before. Figure 5–1 (p. 35) shows that the parasite of a sawfly attacked more cocoons when these hosts were more abundant, but the proportion attacked was less, as shown by the fact that the curve turns towards the right. (It may be shown more explicitly by reading off some approximate values from the curve and converting to percentage of hosts attacked at two or more density levels.) This is an 'inverse' density-relationship; the proportional effect of the factor is less at the higher densities. The *numbers* affected may fall as density rises, or remain the same, or increase, so long as the *percentage* affected is less when density is high. This sort of relationship has also been called 'density-disturbing', or simply 'disturbing'—the effect is the opposite of regulatory.

Another example of an inverse density relationship is associated with 'under-crowding'. If a population is very sparse, its reproduction and increase may be hindered because the sexes meet too seldom for prompt mating of the young females. In some circumstances this leads to a reduced rate of increase. The adverse effect, which is analogous to a sort of mortality, of course becomes more severe as the density falls, or less severe as it rises. To take another example, some animals need to modify their habitat so as to adapt it better to their needs; the fewer the animals, the less effectively may they be able to do this. For instance, grazing animals maintain the grassland on which they thrive; this requires a certain 'grazing pressure' in order to prevent the natural reversion to scrub and woodland which otherwise occurs.

The alert reader will have noticed that in this last example, and perhaps also in the previous one, we are dealing with a *beneficial* effect associated with high (or not-too-low) density. Naturally, the lower the numbers the less the beneficial effect operates, and we treated this as an adverse effect of low density. He may prefer to regard these beneficial effects as examples of a separate sort of density-relationship. If he does this, the effects are still of course density-disturbing (though no longer inverse)—their effect is the opposite of regulatory, for they foster the increase of dense populations and hinder the increase of sparse ones. The latter characteristic is a dangerous one for populations at a very low density.

4.5   Comparison of three basic density-relationships

The essential features of the three major types of relationship discussed above—density-dependent, inverse, and density-independent—may be illustrated and compared in simple diagrams. In Fig. 4–8 the horizontal scales represent population density. The essence of the distinction between the three relationships is shown in (a). For simplicity, density-independence is shown as a horizontal line, although the scatter of points in Fig. 4–7 is more typical. In (b) the vertical scale is in simple numbers instead of in proportional terms; it might for example show numbers dying instead of percentage mortality. The consequences for the graphical form of the three relationships are as shown. In (c) the vertical axis has a scale of beneficial effects or positive aspects of performance. When these beneficial effects are expressed in proportional terms, i.e. effect or performance per individual, as in (c), we have a simple reversal of (a)—a reversal because density-relationships are defined in terms of adverse effects. If the beneficial effect or performance is expressed in straightforward numbers, e.g. as weight of the whole population, or total

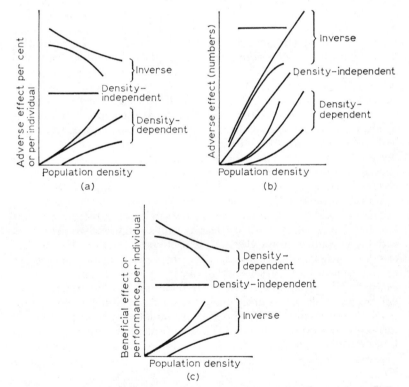

Fig. 4–8   Showing (a) the three basic density relationships, and the forms they take when (b) absolute instead of percentage (or per individual) values are plotted against population density, or (c) beneficial instead of adverse effects are plotted against population density.

number of young produced, the interpretation of the forms of curves is still possible but not so obvious, and it is advisable to convert the performance or effects to values per individual, as in (c), or to calculate the reductions in performance, by subtracting the figures from the highest performance observed, and plot these differences as adverse effects per individual, in form (a).

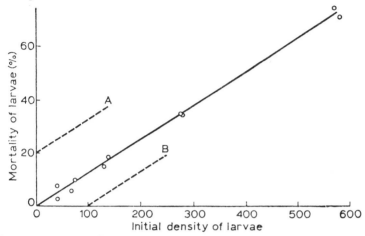

Fig. 4–9   Mortality of larvae of house flies in relation to initial numbers of larvae, in laboratory cultures. Lines A and B explained in text. (Data of BØGGILD, O. and KEIDING, J. (1958). *Oikos*, **9**, 1–25.)

4.6   Forms of density-dependence

Recognizing the qualitative aspects of interactions is only a beginning. The investigator usually tries to describe them in quantitative terms. Special interest attaches to the form of the relationship between density and its effects. The investigator may hope that he will be able to analyse the more complex patterns into simple, elementary components, which he may be able to explain in biological terms.

The simplest relationship is one in which the effect of density is in direct proportion to density itself, as in Fig. 4–9 (main diagonal). If y stands for proportional effect, d for density, and other letters represent constants, the relationship can be written $y = ad$. Lines such as A and B represent the relationships $y = ad + b$, and $y = a(d - c)$, which can also be written $y = ad - e$.

If a relationship appears as a curve on ordinary scales, it can sometimes be transformed to the more convenient straight line form in one way or another, e.g. by using logarithmic scales, as in Fig. 4–10b. The equation here is $\log y = \log a - b \log d$, or $y = ad^{-b}$ in Fig. 4–10a. If, instead of performance, we plot an adverse effect of density, and arrive at a straight line rising towards the right, the relationship is $\log y = \log a + b \log d$.

Fig. 4–10 Fecundity of fruit flies, *Drosophila melanogaster*, in relation to density of flies in a laboratory culture (a), and the same data on logarithmic scales (b). (Data of CHIANG, H. C. and HODSON, A. C. (1950). *Ecol. Monogr.*, **20**, 173–206.)

On non-logarithmic scales the line curves upwards, and the corresponding equation is $y = ad^b$. This was used by Farr, in the 19th century, to express the relation between death-rate and density in human populations.

Density relationships often take on more complex forms than these, sometimes because of uncontrolled variables in the system, sometimes because they are combinations of two or more simpler relationships, sometimes, no doubt, because they are inherently different from the simple forms described above.

4.7 Should regulation be a central topic of population study?

At this point we may pause to glance at the history of a debate that for a long period was a major preoccupation of population ecology. The central question was to what extent populations are regulated (by density-dependent factors) and to what extent they simply fluctuate in response to changing environmental influences. In 1911, Howard and Fiske distinguished the three types of factors now known as density-dependent, density-independent and inverse. They considered the first were essential for the explanation of population balance (regulation).

Nicholson in 1933 and H. S. Smith in 1935 presented more detailed theories on the basis of ideas similar to those of Howard and Fiske. This approach was opposed by W. R. Thompson, who argued that, although density-dependent factors did prevent increase when abundance became unusually high, they were somewhat incidental to the main course of population change, which was essentially a matter of free fluctuation in response to changing environmental conditions.

Meanwhile, Lotka, Volterra and later Nicholson and Bailey made algebraic models of the interactions of predators and prey, or parasites and hosts, based on a few simple assumptions, including the postulate that each responded to changes in density of the other. The models indicated continuous oscillations involving mutual regulation by enemy and victim. Various experimentalists attempted to reproduce such oscillations in laboratory cultures of micro-organisms, mites or insects (cf. Chapter 5).

In the post-war period, a viewpoint very similar to Thompson's has been championed by ANDREWARTHA and BIRCH (1954). They argue that animals simply increase when they can and decline when conditions are unfavourable. Since the environment is heterogeneous, a whole population does not necessarily increase or decline together or equally; this tends to restrict the amount of overall fluctuation. Some density-dependent processes can be more straightforwardly interpreted as, for example, shortage of food, or killing by predators. They prefer more descriptive population study to analysis in terms of density-dependence and regulation. This viewpoint is exemplified in an elementary book on population ecology by ANDREWARTHA (1961). The great majority of other writers on the subject, including NICHOLSON (1954) in a new version of his theory, have adopted some variant of regulation theory. It is not possible here to go into the complexities of this extended debate, now mainly a matter of history. Good discussions of it can be found in DeBACH (1964), LACK (1966) and CLARK et al. (1967), and a sample of the post-war contributions was compiled by McLAREN (1971). There is in fact a wide spectrum of theories extending between the two extremes of Thompson's and Nicholson's early papers, with several offshoots emphasizing special aspects such as genetical change (Pimentel, Chitty) and social self-regulation (Wynne-Edwards).

Now that a number of long-term studies of field populations have been made, attention is focused on the analysis of the relationships involved, and on the construction and testing of mathematical models of these particular examples (see, e.g., VARLEY, GRADWELL and HASSELL, 1973). This process involves an initial choice of assumptions and hypotheses which are being tested by observation and experiment. There is more emphasis on testing and exploring, less on debating.

5 Population Interactions

5.1 Types of interaction

The term 'population interactions' is applied to the influences upon each other of individuals or groups within a population, and also to the influences upon each other of populations of different species. There are other ways too in which different sorts of population interactions may be distinguished, and these various classifications cut across each other. For our present purpose, the first step is to decide what classifications seem relevant to population dynamics. Having done this, we may categorize a given interaction by recording its place in each of the significant classifications.

First, there is the above-mentioned distinction between interactions within a population (intraspecific) and those between different species (interspecific). Most of the examples mentioned in earlier chapters refer to intraspecific relationships, but relations between predator and prey, or herbivore and host plant, are interspecific.

Second, we may distinguish between favourable and unfavourable interactions. We do this on the assumption that abundance and high rates of survival and increase represent success and that an interaction promoting any of these is favourable, while an interaction reducing any of them is unfavourable. When grain mites first break into the germ of wheat grains, there is a co-operative interaction, for the pioneers make this food supply more accessible to the others. The result is favourable—a faster increase in numbers. In a culture of flour beetles, when the adults and larvae eat eggs and pupae, this cannibalistic predation is unfavourable, reducing the rates of survival and increase. The distinction between favourable and unfavourable is deliberately short-sighted. If we enquire whether it may be an advantage in the long run for the population to be hindered from becoming too abundant (and so perhaps from destroying its food supply), the answer may be both hard to discover and complicated.

Third, there is the difference between direct and indirect interactions. Predation is direct. But when animals damage the habitat by destroying shelter or food supply or by excreting toxins into it, the unfavourable effect upon their own or on a different population is indirect, *via* the environment.

Fourth, we may make a three-fold classification as follows. 'One-way' interactions are those in which A influences B, but A is not affected by B, as when, for example, large animals trample upon much smaller ones. Mutual interactions are those in which A and B influence each other in similar ways, e.g. by crowding, or by competing for food. If A and B influence each other in different ways, we need another adjective, such as 'disparate'. For example, if A is a predator and B is its prey, B is a favourable factor for A, while A is an unfavourable one for B.

Remembering the relationships discussed in Chapter 4, we might add another classification, distinguishing between density-related and density-independent interactions. It may be, as some believe, that most population interactions are affected in some degree by density, but the effects may be weak and difficult to demonstrate, in which case, for practical purposes, the interaction must be treated as density-independent. Density-related interactions might be subdivided into density-dependent and inverse, i.e. tending to regulate density or tending to steer it towards the higher or lower extremes.

From time to time the idea of 'competition' has been a subject of discussion among biologists interested in population interactions. They have used the word competition in the following ways:

(1) When numbers of the same or of different species make common use of a resource such as food, shelter or nesting sites, so that some individuals are hindered or deprived by the demands of the others, they are said to compete for the food, etc.

(2) Members of the same or of different species may crowd, jostle or disturb each other, or even make lethal attacks (without being in the relation of true predators and prey). This may be regarded as something different from competition, but is sometimes treated as competition for space.

(3) Relationships such as those mentioned in (1) and (2) above may lead to the elimination from the area or habitat of one species by another. As in all cases of interspecific competition, the relative abundance of the two is important; hence their rates of reproduction and mortality, or of net increase, play a part in determining the outcome. Viewing the relationship as a whole, we may say the two species compete for the habitat, or for existence in the habitat. This may be appropriate even if neither is eliminated, and each survives in the parts where conditions give it the advantage. (It is commonly considered that the competition between species having similar requirements, especially food requirements, will be keener than that between species having different needs. 'Gause's hypothesis' argues from this that species with closely similar requirements cannot persist together in the same habitat. It also follows that competition should be most intense within a species, since many of its individuals have identical requirements.)

There have been differences of opinion whether 'competition' should include only (1), or (1) and (2), or all three of the above ideas. It may seem over-optimistic to expect to establish a precise technical meaning for a word which is used in the same sense and in others in common speech and writing, and indeed this has sometimes led to argument among ecologists about the meanings of terms. It is important that such terms should be clearly defined, or else that the meaning should be made clear enough, for the purpose in hand, by the context in which they are used.

5.2   Interactions of predators and prey, or parasites and hosts

Predators are hunting animals that capture and kill their prey. Parasites are typically much smaller than their hosts and often do not kill them. Parasites include the microbes causing disease, i.e. pathogens. The relationships between populations of pathogens and those of man are dealt with in the science of epidemiology, which is the study of epidemics; in animal populations, outbreaks of microbial disease are called epizootics. Parasitic insects are sometimes called parasitoids, because they are often of the same order of size as their insect hosts, and usually kill them; but they are deposited on or within or near the host, usually as eggs, by the adult female parasite, so they are not predators.

A convenient starting point in the study of predator-prey interactions is to consider the factors influencing the rate of predation. One such factor is the abundance of the prey. If the prey is dense or numerous, a predator will be able to capture as many as it needs with a minimum of effort and time. If the prey is sparse, the predator will have to seek persistently even to catch only a few. As the prey density changes, so will the number taken by the predator. There is an underlying tendency for individual insect predators and parasitoids to take a fixed proportion of the available prey. If this tendency were fully realized, the graph of numbers taken against prey density would be a straight line, sloping upwards as density increased. However, the predators cannot in practice maintain such a response to a persistently rising density of prey; as they become satiated, predators will fail to respond to further increases in prey; moreover, they spend part of their time in 'handling' each captured prey, before they are ready to continue the hunt. Consequently, the potentially straight line turns over as density rises, becoming shallower in slope (Fig. 5–1). The Canadian biologist HOLLING (1959b) imitated this feature of insect predation, with a human 'predator'. Discs of sandpaper were scattered on a table, and the 'predator', blindfolded, searched for them by touch. When the discs were numerous, the 'predator' spent more time in picking them up, and less in searching, so the percentage found in a given time was less. The result was a curve like that in Fig. 5–1.

HOLLING (1959a) also pointed out that vertebrate predators, such as mice and shrews hunting for the pupae of insects in ground litter, responded somewhat differently. When a particular species of prey was sparse, they took only a very low percentage, but at somewhat higher prey densities they took a higher percentage, developing a preference, a skill or

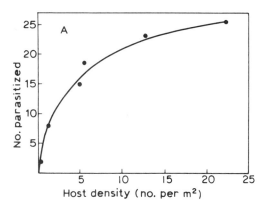

Fig. 5–1 Numbers (not percentage) of sawfly cocoons attacked by parasitic wasps searching for them under trees. (After HOLLING, 1959b, using data of BURNETT, 1958a.)

a habit with respect to the hunting of this species. At much higher densities of prey the percentage captured fell away until the predator was taking a number that no longer increased with higher prey densities. This behaviour tends to produce a characteristic S-shaped curve as shown in Fig. 5–2.

These behaviour patterns of predators are named the 'functional response' (i.e. the response in the predation rate per individual predator to differences in prey density). Another possible reaction of predators to the density of their prey is to become more abundant by reproduction or

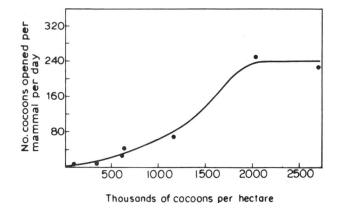

Fig. 5–2 Numbers (not percentage) of cocoons of pine sawfly discovered and destroyed in ground litter per day per individual predator (deer mouse, *Peromyscus*), in relation to the abundance of cocoons. (After HOLLING, 1959a.)

aggregation when or where the prey is more numerous. Graphs of 'numerical responses' take various forms. The total response of a predator to prey density is of course the combined numerical and functional response. Total response is what normally concerns us first in a study of a predator-prey interaction; the analysis into numerical and functional components normally comes later. Holling has extended the analysis of predation by separating out the parts played by searching, pursuit, handling, digestive pauses, hunger, interference between predators, and so on, and constructing flow diagrams that can be a basis for computer programming. For each element, relationships can be formulated algebraically, studied experimentally, and thus given quantitative values appropriate to the situations studied.

Examination of the influence of prey density on the overall rate of predation was the first step in the analysis; it is the only step in this direction in many studies of predator-prey interactions. On the same level, another matter that has sometimes been investigated is the effect of the density of the predators themselves on the rate of predation. In experiments with insect parasitoids, the Canadian biologist BURNETT (1958b) found that the percentage parasitism was linearly proportional to the logarithm of parasite density (Fig. 5–3). If an arithmetic scale had been used instead of a logarithmic one, the points would have fallen about a curve bending over towards the right. This means that the

Fig. 5–3   Percentage of greenhouse whiteflies (*Trialeurodes*) parasitized by the hymenopteron *Encarsia*, in relation to the logarithm of parasite density, in experimental cultures undergoing the parasite-host oscillations. (After BURNETT, 1958b.)

percentage of hosts parasitized fails to increase in proportion to the rise in the number of parasites. In seeking to understand why, we may suspect that the parasites do not produce eggs fast enough, or that they lay many of them in already parasitized hosts, or spend too much time in dealing with each host attacked. Such hypotheses can be tested by experiment.

A common feature of interactions of predators and prey, or of parasites and their hosts, is the appearance of more or less regular cycles of both populations, a little out of phase with each other; each peak of the predator or parasite cycle follows a little after the peak of the prey or host (Fig. 5–4). Usually, each cycle comprises a number of generations. It is convenient to use the term 'oscillations' for cycles of this sort, arising from the interaction of the two populations. They are sometimes called 'reciprocal oscillations', for they arise from the two-way interaction between the two species. Such oscillations were first depicted in the theoretical studies of Lotka, of Volterra (see Appendix to CHAPMAN, 1931), and of NICHOLSON and BAILEY (1935). These authors were concerned with making algebraic models of the changes in numbers of hypothetical predators (or insect parasites) and their prey. It was deduced that the predators would reduce the number of their prey and in turn be themselves reduced by shortage of prey until the latter increased again, and so on. Various experimentalists have set out to reproduce such oscillations with laboratory populations of insects or other convenient animals. Figure 5–4 illustrates one of the more successful examples.

Fig. 5–4 Oscillations of a predatory mite, *Typhlodromus*, and its prey, a plant mite *Eotetranychus*, in a complex laboratory habitat (3 trays of oranges, with some paraffin barriers). (Based on HUFFAKER, C.B. (1958). *Hilgardia*, **27**, 343–83.)

These reciprocal predator-prey (or parasite-host) oscillations involve a special type of regulation. Although the numbers of predators and prey continually rise and fall, these changes are controlled and somewhat regular. Also, while the predator regulates the prey, it is itself regulated by the supply of prey. Each acts as a density-dependent factor upon the other. The oscillations arise because of the delay or persistence of these density-dependent influences. Because of this, predators, insect parasites and the micro-organisms of disease have been called 'delayed density-dependent' factors. The name should be reserved for those actually involved in reciprocal oscillations; so far, such oscillations have been demonstrated chiefly in experiments; although they may be common under natural conditions it is not so easy to identify them with certainty.

Some oscillations of predators and prey look regular enough, but seem not to be really reciprocal. In the north of Europe and Canada, lemmings and other mouse-like mammals fluctuate in a roughly 4-year cycle, and this is reflected in the numbers of their predators, such as the arctic fox and the snowy owl. The snowshoe hare of Canada fluctuates in a 9–10-year cycle, which is reflected in the number of some of its predators, including the lynx, coyote and red fox. It is considered unlikely, however, that the predators are responsible for the cyclic changes in the numbers of the prey. It has been suggested that the snowshoe hare may be involved in a plant-herbivore interaction which generates its oscillations.

5.3   Delayed response as a cause of oscillations

We have remarked that oscillations like those in Fig. 5–4 arise from the delay or persistence of the influence of one upon the other. This is suggested by the fact that cyclic oscillations can be induced in a single species by the delayed effects of competition for a continuous but limiting supply of food. NICHOLSON (1954) demonstrated this with populations of an Australian blowfly in cages in the laboratory (Fig. 5–5). In the example illustrated, the numbers of insects were restricted by the supply of food for the adults. When the flies were numerous, the shortage of food greatly reduced the production of eggs, so the number of flies later fell to a low level; but then the supply of food was enough to enable what flies there were to produce numerous eggs, which developed to a large number of flies, and so on. Although each of the peaks can be taken to represent a single generation (see VARLEY, GRADWELL and HASSELL, 1974), the oscillations are of course not just a reflection of a seasonal life cycle, such as that in Fig. 4–1. If it had not been for the intense competition and its delayed effects, the laboratory cultures of flies would soon have come to

Fig. 5–5   Oscillations in numbers of a laboratory population of a blowfly, *Lucilia*, given ample food for the larvae but a limiting supply of only 0.5 g of ground liver daily for the adults. (Based on NICHOLSON, A.J. (1954).)

be a mixture of all stages in the life cycle. The causes of the oscillations seem to be (1) the delay in the replenishment of the population of adult flies when their numbers fall, a delay imposed by the time taken to develop from eggs to adults, and (2) the failure of adult flies to produce eggs when their numbers were high. Similarly in the mite cultures (Fig. 5–4), there were delays: when the numbers of predators fell, the prey took some time to increase to the level that the sparsity of predators permitted, and the predators themselves required time to respond fully to this increase in prey, and to die down again as the prey became sparser. This is about as far as the explanation can be taken in verbal terms; a more adequate analysis requires mathematical models.

5.4   Competition and self-regulation among higher animals

Mammals and birds have relatively complex patterns of behaviour which are involved in competition for the resources of the habitat, and sometimes provide a regulation of abundance below the level that might be expected from the amount of these resources. Many mammals become more aggressive when their population density rises above a certain (variable) level, and this change is, sometimes at least, associated with a decline in the net rate of reproduction. In D. H. Chitty's studies of the field vole, populations seemed to undergo qualitative changes at high density, and these changes (notably an increased intra-specific aggressiveness and a reduced reproductive success) continued for some generations after the density had 'crashed' again to lower levels. These crashes occur about every fourth year in populations of the vole, as in those of some other rodents.

In many mammals serious fighting is largely avoided; but the animals carry out aggressive displays or 'token' fighting, in face of which one or other of the antagonists usually retreats before real damage is done. This substitution of ritual for real fighting is also common among birds, often associated with the defence of territories in the breeding season. In this way the habitat is divided among a number of breeding pairs, and when it is fully occupied the surplus individuals are forced to leave without breeding. Birds in flocks also compete among themselves for food in the winter, and again serious fighting tends to be avoided: each bird gives way to certain others, but is given precedence by the remainder. Those near the bottom of the 'peck-order' are the first to die when food is in short supply.

In such ways the resources of the habitat are efficiently exploited; if these resources were more equally divided among too many animals, few of the animals might rear their young successfully or survive the season of food shortage. These behaviour patterns tend to ensure that the successful competitors get enough for their needs, and that relatively little of the resources are wasted on individuals that are going to fail. To use the

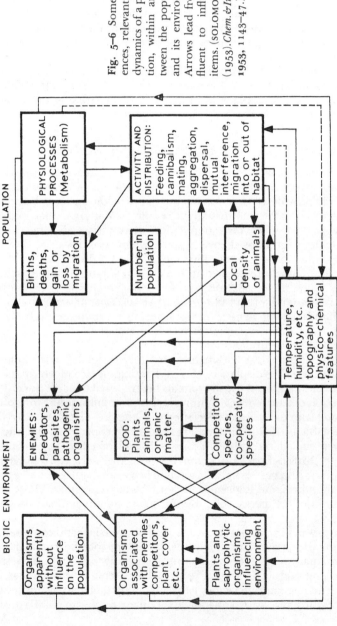

Fig. 5–6 Some influences, relevant to the dynamics of a population, within and between the population and its environment. Arrows lead from influent to influenced items. (SOLOMON, M.E. (1953). *Chem. & Industry,* **1953,** 1143–47.)

POPULATION

BIOTIC ENVIRONMENT

PHYSICAL ENVIRONMENT

PHYSIOLOGICAL PROCESSES (Metabolism)

ACTIVITY AND DISTRIBUTION: Feeding, cannibalism, mating, aggregation, dispersal, mutual interference, migration into or out of habitat

Births, deaths, gain or loss by migration

Number in population

Local density of animals

Temperature, humidity, etc. topography and physico-chemical features

ENEMIES: Predators, parasites, pathogenic organisms

FOOD: Plants animals, organic matter

Competitor species, co-operative species

Organisms apparently without influence on the population

Organisms associated with enemies, competitors, plant cover etc.

Plants and saprophytic organisms influencing environment

terms suggested by A. J. Nicholson, 'scramble' is replaced by 'contest'.

The advantages to the species of this arrangement are as obvious as the advantages of avoiding serious fighting, in which even the victors might be injured. On the basis of these and other considerations, WYNNE-EDWARDS (1962) considers that many animals have evolved ritual social displays which serve to provide an assessment of the size of the population and of the surplus that must be excluded. Many of his arguments are discussed critically by LACK (1966, Appendix).

5·5   Population and environment

We saw in Chapter 4 that populations are influenced by different sorts of factors, some density-dependent, some inverse, many density-indepedent. A population is not only influenced (by its own members, and by outside factors): it also influences its habitat and some at least of the other organisms sharing the habitat: therefore a population and its environment can be seen as a single complex functioning entity—the ecosystem (Fig. 5–6). However, for a particular population, there are usually many factors (including some of the other organisms) which seem to have no significant influence upon it, either directly or indirectly. In judging a particular factor to be irrelevant we may sometimes be mistaken; nevertheless, in a practical study, it is usually necessary to concentrate on the factors that appear to be significant and to ignore the rest, in order to keep the study within practicable bounds. The term 'life system' has been used for the entity comprising a population and the relevant items in its environment (CLARK *et al.*, 1967).

The elements in a life system are connected by a complex network of different influences. For example, a population may be influenced by various natural enemies, on which it also has an influence as a source of food, the environmental temperature may affect the various enemies as well as the population itself, thus modifying their interactions, and so on.

One consequence of these interacting influences is that accounts of the regulation of a population by a particular process, or the degree of fluctuation caused by a particular key factor, are valid only for the set of conditions under which they have been tested. Under other conditions the outcome may be quite different. For example, populations of the grain mite *Acarus siro* are often reduced to the point of extinction by the predatory mite *Cheyletus eruditus*; but the degree of success of this predator in controlling its prey is very much dependent upon the temperature and humidity, and if these are not favourable it cannot prevent the increase of the grain mite. The temperature influences both predator and prey, but in different ways.

In general and simple terms, Fig. 5–7 shows how the two major types of influence upon a population are related to population density and to each other. The arrows again run from the influent to the influenced items.

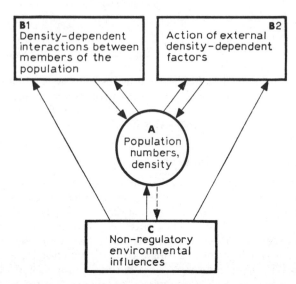

Fig. 5–7 Interactions of population density, density-dependent influences, and non-regulatory environmental influences. Further explanation in text.

Population density (A) is influenced by density-dependent interactions among the members of the population (B1), e.g. in interference or competition: these interactions are themselves influenced by the density of the population (hence the arrows pointing in opposite directions). Similarly, the action of external density-dependent factors (B2) upon the population is shown as being itself influenced by population density. For example, if a predator acts as a density-dependent factor, it is because it responds in a particular way to the level of population density of its prey. Last, but certainly not least, we have the general environmental factors whose influences (C) on the population are not significantly density-dependent; some of these influences may be weakly or inversely related to density (hence the dashed arrow), but they are predominantly density-independent. They include the action of factors like temperature and vegetation, which not only influence mortality and reproduction directly but also 'set the scene' for the population and largely determine how abundant it can be, by influencing the capacity of the habitat and the action of the regulatory density-dependent processes (hence the arrows from C to B1 and B2). These general environmental factors largely determine the conditions in the habitat, and so indirectly determine (a) which density-dependent factors are important in regulation at a particular time and place, and (b) which factors, density-dependent or otherwise, are the key factors, responsible for the main fluctuations in abundance from generation to generation.

Thus we may distinguish between the *regulation* of abundance (by one or more density-dependent processes) and the *determination* of abundance jointly by density-dependent processes and by general environmental factors which set the scene in the habitat and modify the action of the regulatory factors. Regulation may be brought about by a particular predator or by food shortage, for example, but the level of abundance at which this regulation tends to hold the population may vary greatly according to temperature, rainfall, the nature of the vegetation, or other factors.

We must look also to the whole complex, the life system, for a broad understanding of the nature of density-dependent processes. As we have remarked, many of these processes arise from competition within a population for resources in the habitat, e.g. food, refuges or space; the supply per individual depends on how many individuals there are, as well as on the total supply accessible in the habitat, and on the degree to which this may have been reduced by the population. If competitor species are present, they will join in this interaction between animals and resources, to the detriment of the first species. These relationships arise on the one hand from the limited carrying-capacity of the habitat with respect to the species concerned, and on the other hand from the competitive exploitation of the limited resources by this species.

Natural enemies cannot act upon a population as density-dependent (or delayed density-dependent) factors unless the severity of their attack responds in a particular way to the abundance of the population. Their response may be that of a population of animals competing in a density-dependent way for a food supply, the food being the population we are considering; or, as some birds do, they may concentrate on a prey species when (or where) it is abundant, but tend to ignore this species when (or where) it is sparse.

Density-dependence may be regarded as a relationship maintaining a stable equilibrium of numbers. If numbers rise above or fall below a particular equilibrium level, a density-dependent process geared to that level will intensify or relax, tending to steer the population back towards the equilibrium level. But it must be stipulated that, because of changes in the environment and often in the animals themselves, the equilibrium level tends to change continually, so that it would be difficult to identify it at any time: it is a stable but moving equilibrium.

In delayed density-dependence, the operative factor comes into action slowly or weakly at first, allowing some continuation of the rise of numbers above equilibrium level; then it overshoots the mark, forcing the numbers below the equilibrium level before relaxing. In this way it imposes oscillations on the population as well as regulating it.

6 Plant Population Dynamics

6.1 Similarities and differences between plant and animal populations

For the purposes of population dynamics, plants differ from animals in some respects, and resemble them in others. If we choose particular features for the comparison (e.g. reproduction, competition) we often find both resemblances and differences.

Like those of animals, populations of any one species of plant are found in particular types of habitat. Plants tend to be specially dependent on certain soil characteristics (acidity, water regime etc.), whereas many animals are dependent primarily on the presence of a particular type of vegetation, and some require one particular species of plant.

Individual plants mature, reproduce and die. Plants, like animals, include ephemeral and long-lived species and, like animals, often produce large numbers of potential young, most of which never become established. Many plants reproduce or extend themselves vegetatively, by means of bulbils, runners, rhizomes etc., giving rise to mats of vegetation in which it is difficult to decide where individuals begin and end. But aggregation of most plants arises largely because of their immobility as individuals, in contrast to most animals, which are free to disperse. The fixity of plants makes some sorts of population study easier than with animals which are frequently on the move.

Like animals, plants compete for food materials and other requisites; in general, they compete more for light and moisture than animals do. Plants are in general more variable in size, according to the environmental conditions and the intensity of competition.

Plant populations, like those of animals, wax and wane as conditions change, but often more slowly. Like animals, they are restricted in number or in biomass by the limited supply of things they require, such as food, water, access to light etc. (hence the competition for these requisites). Like animals, they may be limited by the attacks of natural enemies—herbivores, and possibly some pathogenic micro-organisms.

Like populations of animals, those of plants are made up of individuals differing in genetic constitution, except in clones (a clone is a group descended from an individual parent by asexual reproduction); these are commoner in plant than in animal populations. Genetic differences between individuals are the raw material of evolution by natural selection. This process is generally envisaged as influencing the genetic pattern of a species over a wide area and on a time-scale reckoned in thousands of years. But there is evidence, in both plants and animals, of much more rapid, though smaller, genetic changes, particularly in response to the conditions of a newly invaded or a newly changed habitat. Some investigators claim that rapid changes in the genetic pattern of a population may, to some extent, reflect changes in its density, and so may enter into the dynamics of its regulation.

6.2 Density effects and competition among plants

To say that plants compete for resources is to imply the existence of density effects comparable to those among animals. Such effects have been demonstrated and measured experimentally. As among animals, different density effects vary in form when graphed and have been interpreted by means of various algebraic equations. Two examples will suffice to show their similarity in principle to the corresponding relationships of animals.

In Canberra, Australia, DONALD (1961) set up experiments with clover on small field plots, to compare the effects of different plant densities upon yield (the crop of plant material that could be harvested). He supplied ample water and nutrients to the plots, so there was no competition until the plants grew large enough to compete with each other for light. In Fig. 6–1a, the lowest line represents the early, non-

Fig. 6–1 Yield (dried crop) from clover plants at various densities, competing for light in experimental plots; (a) yield per unit area, (b) yield per plant. ((a) After DONALD, 1961; courtesy of Cambridge Univ. Press. (b) Based on same data.) One sq. link = 405 cm².

competitive stage, in which the yield per unit area was directly proportional to the number of plants involved. The two upper lines show how, as time passed and the plants grew larger and began to cast shade upon each other, the yield per unit area in the denser plots (on the right in the graph) became less and less dependent on the number of plants there, and after 181 days had approached a constant maximal value. The total amount of the crop was finally determined by the supply of sunlight; if one plot had more plants than another, then these more numerous plants were smaller. In Fig. 6–1b, these results are converted to a form comparable with that of Fig. 4–10a.

The second example concerns experiments in which PALMBLAD (1968) reared single-species populations of plants in pots. He started with 1, 5, 50, 100 and 200 seeds per pot, and observed the plants that grew from them. Among other things, he recorded the number of seeds formed per plant which achieved the reproductive phase. When his observed values are graphed against the initial density of seeds per pot (Fig. 6–2), the points follow a curve analogous to those of Fig. 6–1b.

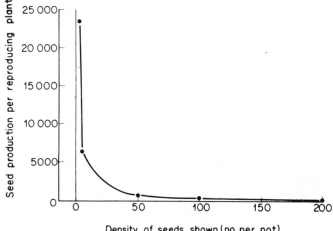

Density of seeds shown (no. per pot)

Fig. 6–2   Results of experiments with shepherd's purse (*Capsella*) in plant pots. Data of PALMBLAD (1968).

When plants of the same species compete, the size of the individual plants may vary in relation to density, and so may the number of seeds produced by each. But the seeds, like the eggs of animals, tend to be constant in size for each species.

The above are instances of density effects associated with intraspecific competition. Interspecific competition also occurs among plants: this has been inferred both from field observations and from experiments. What happens may depend a good deal on whether the different species begin growth at the same time, or one is already established when another begins. When a crop is sown, crop and weeds may begin growth together. Such a situation was studied experimentally by ASPINALL and MILTHORPE (1959), using spring barley and white persicaria (*Polygonum lapathifolium*) emerging on the same day in pots. Figure 6–3 shows the growth in dry weight of barley surrounded by four persicaria, and of persicaria surrounded by four barley (not enough for significant competition), compared with the growth of each species when surrounded by 128 of the other. The curves show that the effect of persicaria on barley was relatively slight, whereas the effect of barley on persicaria was great. This result arose from the fact that the persicaria at emergence was much smaller than the barley, and could not overcome this initial disadvantage. In such competition, the size of the seeds of the different species is important, for plants with larger seeds have correspondingly larger seedlings giving them an advantage in competition with small-seeded plants.

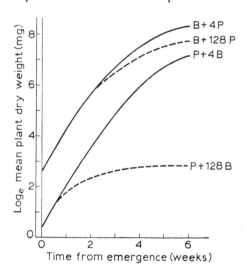

Fig. 6–3   Relationship with time of the logarithms of dry weight per plant of barley (B) surrounded by 4 or 128 white persicaria plants (P), and of persicaria surrounded by 4 or 128 barley plants. (After MILTHORPE, 1961; courtesy of Cambridge Univ. Press.)

As with animals, the influence of plants upon each other is not necessarily adverse. Apart from some being dependent on others parasitically or for support, some do better in the presence of other species than in a single-species stand. For example, HARPER (1960) found that when he sowed seeds of poppy (*Papaver*) with wheat, under some conditions more poppy plants were produced than when poppy was sown alone: it seemed that the presence of the wheat plants increased the number of sites suitable for the development of poppy plants.

It is often found that competition is more severe between members of the same species than between members of different species. In stands of poppies, HARPER and McNAUGHTON (1962) showed that the chances of establishment of a particular species from seed were higher in the presence of other species of poppy than in pure culture, for a given total density. WHITTINGTON and O'BRIEN (1968) found that mixed species of grasses gave a higher yield than did one species alone. We may interpret this as meaning that plants of the same species competed more intensely than did those of different species, because their requirements were more similar (cf. p. 33). Or we may say that the mixed species, having different requirements and capabilities, exploited the available resources more completely than could a single species.

The ultimate outcome of competition between two species may be the displacement of one of them from the habitat. Field observations continued over a long enough period often show some species becoming more abundant while others become sparser. Sometimes a population of one species may be seen to advance upon and displace that of another species: WATT (1955) observed a continuous front of bracken invading and gradually replacing a stand of heather (rabbit grazing may have been a complicating factor).

Competitive displacement may also be demonstrated experimentally. SAGAR and HARPER (1961) removed grasses with a selective herbicide in patches of various grassland habitats near Oxford, to test the effect of this upon plantains (*Plantago*). They also sowed seeds of plantain in existing grassland. The results suggested that in some of the communities the grasses had an important influence on the presence or absence of particular species of plantains (as well as on their abundance when present). In the laboratory, CLATWORTHY and HARPER (1962) demonstrated the exclusion of one species of duckweed (*Lemna*) by another. They found, incidentally, that the winner in such a contest between species was not necessarily the one that was denser in pure cultures. (The same has been observed in experiments with different species of flour beetles: cf. PARK (1955, 1962).)

6.3   Regulation of plant populations

In relatively simple situations such as in laboratory cultures, it is obvious that the limited supply of space or of nutrients sets a limit to the number of individuals that can exist there, even allowing for the often stunted size of crowded individuals. Well-developed density effects, such as those referred to in §6.2, can exert regulation if other factors allow the population to reach the levels of abundance at which they operate.

Among the natural enemies of plants, certain herbivores at least are

Fig. 6-4 A stand of prickly pear (*Opuntia*) before and after attack by caterpillars of *Cactoblastis* (*centre*). (Reproduced by courtesy of Survey Branch, Lands Department, Queensland and C.S.I.R.O., Canberra.

known to act as regulatory agents. A clear witness to this is the success achieved in the economic control of certain weeds by the introduction of appropriate insects. A classic example of such biological control is the introduction of the moth *Cactoblastis* to eastern Australia to deal with prickly pear, a group of cacti comprising several species of *Opuntia* (Fig. 6–4). These introduced plants had by 1925 taken over some 12 million hectares of country with their thickets of spiny lobes. When *Cactoblastis* became established, its caterpillars rapidly destroyed the major pest cacti, and it increased and spread to surrounding areas. The economic problem was thus effectively solved by the late 1930s. But the insects did not completely eradicate the prickly pear. There were usually plants which escaped attack and continued growing; the stands developing from these were usually found at a later date by egg-laying *Cactoblastis* moths, and were demolished by the caterpillars before reaching any considerable size. (From many areas the survivors of insect attack were removed by cultivation.)

Another well-known example is the control of St. John's wort, *Hypericum perforatum*, by means of leaf-beetles of the genus *Chrysolina*. This weed is a pest of grazing land in many parts of the world, displacing useful forage, and poisoning stock when eaten in quantity. In California the beetles have exerted a spectacular degree of control, reducing St. John's wort to about a hundredth of its former abundance. They have been successful too in some parts of Australia, though not in others. In many of the areas where the weed persists, the beetles keep it at a much reduced level of abundance.

For our present purpose, the point of these examples is the evidence they provide of the great impact that insects can make upon the abundance of plants. In many studies of plant populations the possible influence of insects has been neglected.

Larger herbivores should also be considered. When the appearance and spread of myxomatosis in Britain in the 1950s removed the rabbits from many parts of the country, some of the consequent changes in the vegetation were obvious to anyone who knew the areas concerned, and many less obvious changes were recorded by plant ecologists. Some grasses and woody plants increased in size and abundance, and other species lost ground in competition with these. There was a noticeable decline of ragwort (*Senecio jacobaea*); and in many places where rabbits have re-established themselves the ragwort has again become a prominent feature (and sometimes a danger to stock).

A method of demonstrating the influence of grazing on vegetation is to set up enclosures. Where grazers such as rabbits or sheep are important, their exclusion from plots produces a rapid and striking increase in the amount of vegetation, with changes too in the relative abundance of different species.

7 Economic and Social Population Problems

7.1 Crops as populations

Cereals, vegetables, fruits and other useful crops are mostly grown in monoculture, i.e. as plant populations of a single species. By dint of cultivation, use of fertilizers and judicious spacing, the grower aims to reap the maximum harvest per hectare of land, and to maintain a high level of quality. As standards rise, commonsense and experience need more and more to be reinforced by research, including research into the relations of the plants to one another, as members of a population. Obviously, too sparse a crop will waste land and encourage weeds. But too dense a sowing or planting will also waste material, and give rise to unfavourable density effects and wasteful competition (§6.2). One of the aims of the plant breeder is to develop varieties that will tolerate high densities with the minimum of harmful competition. One of the functions of research is to clothe these bare principles with quantitative information, applying to particular crops, soils, climates and methods.

At the same time, since competition tends to be most intense between organisms with the same requirements, there are advantages in growing different crops together. (There are other advantages too: one crop may protect a second, or provide useful nutrients, as clover provides extra nitrogen for grass in a pasture.) Sometimes these benefits more than offset the advantages of monoculture, which is simpler to manage and more amenable to mechanical husbandry.

7.2 Populations of pests

Any animal that damages crops or domestic animals or disturbs our own comfort or health may be called a pest. But, economically, there is a vast difference between a major pest and one that is rare or incidental. This difference is chiefly a matter of abundance. With a few exceptions, a major pest is one that is abundant, or that can become so at times and in certain circumstances.

Many pest populations are notably unstable: periods of low density are interrupted by occasional and sometimes sudden increases ('outbreaks'; cf. Fig. 4–2). A pre-requisite for this sort of population pattern is a high rate of increase under favourable conditions. As we have seen, this may be achieved either by the production of numerous eggs or young by each female, or by a rapid passage through several generations, or, of course, both.

The reasons why some species are abundant or common in a particular region while others are sparse or rare are seldom clearly known. In principle, it is clear that various characteristics of a species and of its environment may be important in determining its abundance, e.g. (1) its requirements of food, physical conditions, cover, breeding sites etc., and the extent to which the environment fulfils these requirements, (2) its reproductive capacity under favourable conditions, and (3) the presence and abundance of various natural enemies, competitors and pathogens. For a few animals that have been intensively studied it is possible to specify which factors chiefly determine their abundance, but for most species this remains to be discovered.

Many species that reach high densities as pests of cultivation do not seem to be abundant in their natural environments. Natural communities tend to be complex, with a varied flora and fauna. Whether in virtue simply of this complexity, or because in addition natural communities have evolved a self-adjusting balance, it seems that any tendency for particular species of animals to be very abundant is commonly offset by a series of opposing influences. It has been claimed that predators and parasites are limited by the availability of prey, while herbivores are limited by the attacks of such natural enemies. If this were accepted without qualifications, we should have to explain the success of biological control of weeds as being made possible only by introducing herbivorous insects without their natural enemies. Be that as it may, there is no doubt that many species reach much higher levels of abundance on crops than they do under natural conditions. In contrast to the stabilizing complexity of nature, monoculture provides a simplified or impoverished set of conditions, with relatively few of the controlling mechanisms that operate in nature. Moreover, the environment of monoculture is relatively uniform; if it is favourable to a pest, it is likely to be widely favourable, whereas in nature the habitat is much more varied, and is less likely to be favourable everywhere at once. Again, the use of insecticides to control the pests often kills most of their natural enemies, so that there are few natural controls to rely on if the chemicals should fail (and they often do fail, after a time, through the development of insecticide resistance in the pests). In managed forest, the recurrence of severe outbreaks of pests in single-species stands has led to the adoption of a policy of mixed-species woodlands in many areas.

The way in which the above general points apply to particular pests must of course be discovered by research. When this is done, the results often suggest ways of improving the control of the pest. For example, the bullfinch is a pest of orchards in Britain, stripping off the buds of trees and bushes in the latter part of the winter. Since these birds do not move far from their home ground, their numbers can be usefully reduced by trapping or shooting in the orchards and surrounding woodland. The natural tendency has been to trap or shoot at the time when the damage is being done. But research by NEWTON (1967) at Oxford confirmed that the bullfinch feeds on the seeds of various plants such as nettles and docks in early winter, and that when these supplies are exhausted they move on to ash seeds. The crop of ash seeds varies greatly from year to year; in roughly alternate years there is a very poor crop. It is in these winters that the bullfinch, running short of seeds, turns to buds as a major item of food, preferring the buds of the cultivated fruit plants to those of wild trees and shrubs. Newton pointed out that if orchardists are to rely on reducing the local numbers of bullfinches, they should do this at the beginning of winter, before the birds have depleted the stock of weed seeds. Then the survivors will be less dependent on the ash seeds, less likely to exhaust them, and so less likely to turn to the orchards in late winter.

7.3   Biological control of pests

The biological control of pests, by the introduction and establishment of parasites, predators, or pathogens, has been more often used than has the biological control of weeds, described in §6.3. One of the most successful and best-known examples is the control of the cottony-cushion scale, *Icerya purchasi*, in California by the introduction of the predatory ladybird beetle *Rodolia cardinalis* in the late nineteenth century (Fig. 1–1). Scale insects are related to the aphids, and suck the sap from plants. *Icerya* is a pest of citrus trees; a heavy infestation can severely damage the shoots, even killing the trees at times. It forms a conspicuous white waxy bag in which numerous eggs are laid. It is native to Australia, from which it was accidentally introduced on young trees to California. There it flourished remarkably, and became a serious threat to orange groves. The entomologist A. Koebele travelled to Australia to seek its natural enemies, and sent back the *Rodolia* ladybird. Where this was released in California it rapidly reduced the populations of *Icerya* to such a low level that it was often hard to find any. Outbreaks of the scale occurred from time to time in places that the ladybird had not reached, or where it had been killed by insecticides; but the introduction of the ladybird to the infested orchards has demonstrated again and again its ability to bring about rapid and entirely satisfactory control of the pest. In its native Australia the scale is usually not abundant, and there is no doubt that *Rodolia* and other natural enemies are at least partly responsible for its low numbers. When it was taken to California without its natural enemies, it multiplied alarmingly, and was regulated only at a very high density at the limits of its food supply. When the ladybird was introduced *Icerya* was reduced to very low numbers, and generally held there, its abundance regulated at a much lower level by this predator.

An interesting short account of some recent examples of biological control is given by WATERHOUSE and WILSON (1968). For a comprehensive treatment see DeBACH (1964), or his shorter and more readable book of 1974. Many of the big successes in biological control have been with species of pests or of weeds that, like *Icerya*, were introduced to new regions without their natural enemies. The introduction of suitable parasites, predators or herbivores has restored the missing regulatory factors which keep their numbers at a low level in their native environment.

In Britain, most pests are native to the region, and this is probably one reason why relatively few attempts at biological control have been made. The minute parasitic wasp *Aphelinus mali* was introduced in the 1920s to control the woolly aphis of apple trees, but for climatic or other reasons it was not the success that it was in various warmer countries. In heated glasshouses, useful control of the whitefly *Trialeurodes vaporariorum* (related to scales and aphids) has sometimes been achieved by the introduction of another minute parasitic wasp, *Encarsia formosa*; and the glasshouse red spider mite, *Tetranychus urticae*, a pest of cucumbers and other crops, has been successfully controlled in a large number of glasshouses by the introduction of *Phytoseiulus persimilis*, a predatory mite from Chile. WYATT (1974) gives a convenient account of this work, which has been developed at the Glasshouse Crops Research Institute at Littlehampton. The parasites or predators are released together with some numbers of the pest to provide their food, carefully distributed over the plants; the timing of the introduction is critical.

Besides insect parasites and predators, pathogenic bacteria and viruses have occasionally been used with success in the control of insect pests (DeBACH, 1964). For example, the European pine and spruce sawflies have been successfully controlled in parts of Canada by introduction of appropriate viruses. As a class, viruses have the virtue of being highly specific, so that no danger to beneficial insects is involved. The bacterium *Bacillus thuringiensis* has been used with some success against various caterpillars (BURGES and HUSSEY, 1971). Attempts at biological control with fungi have been made, but with limited success, perhaps chiefly because they remain effective only under moist conditions. Promising advances have been made towards the use of fungi to control harmful fungi in living trees and in cut stumps.

In recent years a number of new types of biological control have been tried, and used successfully in a few instances (JONES and SOLOMON, 1974). One method is to release large numbers of adults of the pest species made reproductively sterile by exposure to a radioactive source or to a chemical sterilant; if enough of the normal population mate with the sterile individuals instead of with each other, the reproductive rate will fall below that necessary to maintain the population, and the numbers will decline with increasing rapidity to zero.

7.4   The impact of modern insecticides

The control of pests by means of toxic chemicals, applied as sprays, dusts or as gases, has been practised for over a century. Some of these measures were quite successful in reducing damage by the pests to acceptable levels, but many pests were not adequately controlled.

The introduction in the years since 1940 of a series of very successful new insecticides, beginning with DDT, marked a new era in the history of pest control. For a time, it seemed to many people that biological methods of control could be discarded. However, serious weaknesses in the strategy of control by insecticides gradually claimed the attention of economic entomologists. The killing of natural enemies enabled insects and mites that had been obscure minor pests to become a major problem. For example, the use of DDT in orchards to control codling moth and other pests led to severe outbreaks of fruit tree red spider mite.

Another difficulty in the intensive use of insecticides is one already mentioned—the appearance of resistant strains of pests. All species exhibit inheritable individual variations, and there is often a minute fraction of an insect or mite population which carries genes conferring a relatively high resistance to the pesticide employed. If these few individuals survive a treatment, the population derived from them will be more resistant than the original one. If the same insecticide is used repeatedly, the process of selection will continue and the population will become increasingly resistant. Such an increase of resistance may be both rapid and striking: strains that, by certain criteria, are hundreds or even thousands of times as resistant as the original population may be developed. The nature of this resistance has been intensively studied by biochemists and geneticists. Biochemically, it has been shown in some cases to involve breakdown of the insecticide by the insect's metabolic processes. Genetically, it has been shown to be inherited in some instances as a simple Mendelian unit factor, in others by a more complex genetic pattern. Occasionally the factor selected has proved to be a behaviour pattern which enables the pest to escape fatal contact with the insecticide. Physiological resistance to one insecticide confers resistance also to others that are chemically related to it; hence, although it is often possible to deal with the situation by changing to a different type of insecticide, there are relatively few groups at present available which differ sufficiently from each other for this purpose; there is therefore a danger that, as resistance is developed to several categories of chemicals in turn, some pests may exhaust the available armoury of insecticides.

7.5   Integrated control and pest management

Largely as a result of the above difficulties associated with complete reliance on insecticides, many economic biologists have adopted, or returned to, a more comprehensive strategy of pest control (SOLOMON, 1973). A first step in this direction was the use of fewer applications of insecticides, or the use of more selective ones than the 'broad spectrum' compounds such as DDT, so as to allow the survival of parasites and predators that can make a valuable contribution to the reduction of pests. The seasonal timing of insecticide treatments can also be chosen so as to reduce the damage done to useful natural enemies. Another way of ensuring the survival of some natural enemies is to leave untreated certain patches in or around a crop, a policy that is justified if we have reason to think that the enemies will more than compensate for the pests that are spared with them.

Such a modification of chemical measures to allow more scope for natural control factors is what was first called 'integrated control'; but this term came to include the combination of chemical measures with biological control organized by the introduction of predators, parasites or pathogens; it now includes any combination of different methods of control, and sometimes even refers to the integration of the control measures against two or more different pests or pathogens of a crop.

For an example of the integration of biological and chemical control we may refer back to the biological control of the spider mite *Tetranychus urticae* on cucumbers in glasshouses by the introduced predatory mite *Phytoseiulus*. As the plants grow up, some of them approach the top (ridge) of the glasshouse where the warm conditions at times in summer can lead to failure of the predator. One way of dealing with this situation is to spray the tips near the ridge with the acaricide tetradifon, which controls the spider mites with little damage to the predator (HUSSEY and BRAVENBOER, 1971).

A more comprehensive view of integrated control underlies the life system approach (CLARK *et al.*, 1967). This idea is in line with the views of many ecologists; it seeks to take due account of all significant elements in the pest-crop-environment situation, not only selective insecticides and natural enemies, but also methods of husbandry, the possibility of developing varieties having a greater inherent resistance to attack, and any other factor which it may be possible to modify advantageously. In such an approach, the ecology of the pest, and especially its population dynamics, calls for special attention.

The life system means, in short, the parts of the ecosystem that are relevant to the activities of a pest and to its control. The mere adoption of this comprehensive viewpoint does not of course automatically provide a means of modifying the situation so as to control the pest. For any one pest and crop, expensive and time-consuming research is required to fill out this broad picture with factual information. Meanwhile, of course, practical pest control, by the best means at present available, must be continued.

7.6   Man as a predator

It is only relatively recently in the history of man, in the Neolithic cultural stage, that the gathering of plant food and the hunting of animals ceased to be the basic activity of most human communities, and were superseded by agriculture and the domestication of animals. The earlier ways of life have of course not disappeared, and indeed some forms of hunting—e.g. that of fish and whales from the sea—have greatly increased in modern times. Primitive man probably lacked the skills and numbers to endanger the survival of the species he preyed upon. Today man is very differently placed in this respect. Modern vessels and techniques have enabled him to reduce the abundance of some marine fish to a level at which further fishing is in danger of becoming an uneconomic activity; for lack of international agreement, the whaling industry appears to be foundering, and the blue whale of the southern seas has been so reduced that the survival of the species is in doubt. Excessive and wasteful slaughter led to near-extinction of the once abundant bison in North America.

Although the ethical, social and political aspects of these matters are a legitimate concern of biologists, here we must concentrate on the problems of population dynamics which are involved. If a predator becomes so efficient that its prey cannot maintain itself, the predator must subsist on other food, or else die out itself. Man should use his wits and his social organization to ensure that he does not continue to endanger the survival of valuable prey species. He must study the population dynamics of his prey, estimate realistically the degree of exploitation it can stand without loss of yield, and solve the problems of international agreement.

British marine biologists have been concerned with the effects of over-fishing by our own and other European fleets in the seas around our coasts and northwards to Iceland. The cessation of fishing during the two world wars led to great increases in the stock of fish in these seas, by over 100 per cent in some areas. The late E. S. Russell summarized the dynamics of these populations in the equation

$$S_2 = S_1 + (A + G) - (C + M),$$

where S_2 is the weight of fish large enough to be retained by the meshes of the particular nets used in the fishery, at the end of the year; S_1 is the corresponding weight at the beginning of the year; A represents the addition to the stock provided by young fish growing up to a catchable size; G is the addition provided by the growth of fish beyond the minimum catchable size; C is the weight of fish caught during the year; and M is the weight lost by natural death of some of the fish that are not caught. The equation is simply a convenient list of the gains and losses that must be estimated and set against each other as factors influencing the exploitable fish population. A few numerical examples of the influence of different rates of fishing on the population, and references to the main works on this subject, are given by HARDY (1959; see also PHILLIPSON, 1966, pp. 51–3).

7.7   Populations of domesticated animals

Although the transition from hunting to the domestication of animals may have begun 10,000 or more years ago, it is still going on. More species are being domesticated and the numbers of individuals reared are continually increasing. There is also an intermediate stage, the culling of herds that are wild but 'managed' as regards their abundance and range of wandering. Fully domesticated animals have been spread widely through the world but have not always done well. It has been suggested that the management of some of the wild herbivores in parts of Africa might be the most economic way of exploiting the land for man's benefit. On the island of Rhum, off the west coast of Scotland, wild red deer have been found to give a better yield than sheep did there.

Stock-raisers whose animals are free-ranging are concerned with the carrying capacity of the land—the number of grazing sheep or cattle per acre that it will maintain permanently. With more intensive methods the animals are maintained at an artificially high density in fenced areas, moved periodically from a grazed area to a rested one, and provided with supplementary feed in various forms.

In free-range or in natural conditions, the relationship of grazing animals to the vegetation of their pastures is similar to that of predators and prey in one respect—that the ultimate limits to the abundance of the grazers are set by their food supply. This form of limitation may seldom operate under truly natural conditions, where predators tend to keep the density of grazers at a much lower level than their food supply would do. But when these natural controlling agents are eliminated, the food supply will be the limiting factor unless human predation—planned culling of the herds—is applied so as to keep the numbers down to a reasonable level. This has not always been done, and in many regions sheep, goats or cattle have been allowed to overtax and degrade the land.

The rate of increase of animals is another major concern of the grazer and stockbreeder. A high rate of reproduction provides a large annual surplus that can be killed or marketed. The rate of increase of different species of farm animals varies enormously. In her first 3 years a cow normally produces one calf. But a sow will produce her first litter at 9 months, and thereafter have two litters per year, with an average of 8 young in each; so in the first 3 years, if all her descendants were kept and allowed to breed, their total would be 2220 (HAMMOND, 1955).

7.8   Human populations

In earlier sections of this book we noticed the following aspects of the dynamics of animal populations. (1) Numbers tend to increase up to the capacity of the environment, i.e. up to the limit of supply of some essential resource, often food. (2) But the capacity of the environment may undergo frequent fluctuations, and sometimes a permanent change, due to changes in weather or climate, or because of changes in the vegetation or the effects of various animals. The response of a population to such changes cannot usually occur all at once; part at least of it requires time to develop, especially when the response is a reproductive increase. Moreover, numbers in a population are often held below the level they could otherwise reach, as a result of (3) the competition of other species that take a part of the limiting resources, (4) interference or predation among its own members, or (5) the attacks of predators, parasites or pathogens. Some or all of these processes may operate in combination.

In human populations all of these phenomena have been evident at various times and places. (1) Hunger, malnutrition and recurrent famines in certain regions have testified to man's tendency to increase to the limits of the current resources of the local environment, although other factors have often been involved, e.g. migration, the adverse effects of disease on productive efficiency, also (2) effects of adverse weather on crops, and damage to the environment by over-exploitation and misuse. (3) Our food supply is reduced by the activities of competitor species—pests that attack livestock, growing crops and stored food. (4) Warfare, ritual sacrifice and infanticide represent human versions of interference and predation within the species. (5) Predators of man are scarcely a significant factor nowadays, but in some regions diseases such as malaria (due to parasites transmitted by mosquitoes), sleeping sickness (due to parasites transmitted by tsetse flies in Africa) and infectious diseases like smallpox (caused by a virus) still have an important influence on man's abundance.

In spite of the various processes opposing its growth, the human population has increased slowly through the ages. Since the seventeenth century, with rapid technical advances in control over the environment and the causes of disease, the rate of increase has continuously accelerated. The world population is roughly estimated to have been 906 million in 1800, 1171 million in 1850, 1608 million in 1900, and 2407 million in 1950. Not only have our numbers continued to grow, but the proportional rate of increase has been rising: the above estimates represent increases of 29 per cent, 37 per cent and 50 per cent in these three equal periods. This acceleration is still evident, for the estimated population in 1972 was 3782 million. By studying recent trends, demographers have made extrapolations into the future. One such projection suggests a total of about 5000 million in 1985, and another suggests about 7000 million in the year 2000.

The above figures for the total population of past years are inaccurate, because they are based partly on unreliable and incomplete censuses in many parts of the world. But the more complete and reliable figures from the advanced countries confirm the general trend, and there is little basis at present for any expectation that the rate of world population increase is about to decline.

An increase in abundance can come about by way of a rise in percentage reproductive rate, while the percentage death rate remains steady, or by way of a decline in the death rate while the reproductive rate remains unchanged; or both may increase, or both decrease, so long as the reproductive rate increases more, or declines less, than the death rate does. United Nations statistics show that birth rates and death rates have both been declining (Table 4). The death rate in the more advanced

Table 4 Crude birth rates and death rates per 1000 of population in five countries. Figures from United Nations Demographic Yearbook (1948, 1960 and 1972)

Years	1932	[1]1958,[2]1959,[3]1960	1965–70	[1]1970,[2]1971,[3]1972
United Kingdom				
birth rate	15.8	[2]16.9		[3]14.9
death rate	12.3	[2]11.7		[3]11.9
U.S.A.				
birth rate	17.4	[3]23.6		[3]15.6
death rate	10.9	[3]9.5		[3]9.4
Chile				
birth rate	34.0	[2]35.4		[1]29.6
death rate	22.7	[2]12.5		[1]9.4
India				
birth rate	33.6	[1]39.1	42.8	
death rate	21.4	[1]19.4	16.7	
Japan				
birth rate	32.9	[2]17.5		[2]19.2
death rate	17.7	[2]7.4		[2]6.6

countries seems to be moving towards a value appreciably below 10 per 1000 per year. To prevent further population increase, the birth rate would have to decline to the same level. The crude death rate, i.e. yearly deaths per 1000 of population, is a faulty index of mortality since it takes no account of the age composition of the population or of the incidence of deaths in different age-groups. Because of this, demographers prefer to construct a life table and derive from it the mean expectation of life at birth. This index shows a steady increase, for example from 44.6 years for females in England and Wales in 1871–80 to 71.5 years in 1950–52 and 75.1 years in 1969–71, confirming the trend suggested by the cruder death rate figures. It seems, then, that birth rates have been declining, but death rates have been declining more. The reduction in death rates is attributable to the improvement in the living standards and hygiene in many parts of the world, and to the even more widespread application of modern advances in medicine and in the control of malaria-carrying mosquitoes, for example, by means of modern insecticides. The overall rate of increase would have been greater than it has been but for the effects of wars and famines and the epidemics that have tended to follow in their train. There is, however, another and very potent factor operating to reduce the birth rate. This is the widespread preference for small families by people who have had the benefits of at least a moderately good standard of living and education, and who are no longer faced with the probability of high mortality among their children.

We have seen that, although there has been an overall decline in birth rate, the fall in death rate has been faster, and that consequently the population is increasing more and more rapidly. This is specially so in the poorer countries, where the resultant hardship is greatest and the food supply already insufficient. It is the relation of numbers to food supply that gives the greatest cause for anxiety. There is a race between increasing population and increasing food supply, the latter brought about by improving methods of production and the fuller exploitation of some sources such as fisheries. In the period 1955 to 1973, food production has risen at a roughly similar rate, overall, in advanced and underdeveloped countries. In the developed countries the rise in population has been slower than this, so that the food production per head has increased on average by about 1.5 per cent per annum; whereas in the underdeveloped countries the rise in population has been almost as fast as the rise in food production, so that the increase in food production per head has been only about 0.4 per cent per annum, and in Africa there has been a downward trend since 1961. Clearly these latter countries need a faster increase in food production and slower population growth, if the severe food shortages they suffer are to be corrected.

Another important aspect of this problem is not directly related to population, but rather to economics and politics. That is the uneven distribution of the available food. Even in some of the wealthier countries, sections of the population suffer malnutrition, whilst others have more food than is good for them. In most of the poorer countries this contrast is far more striking. Countries that produce a surplus of food could often produce more still, but difficulties of economics and transport have to be overcome in order to make the effort worth-while to the growers and get the surplus to all the places where it is needed. Since these problems cannot easily be solved, it is important that in each region the population should remain within the limits set by that region's current ability to produce or import an adequate food supply. Improvements in food production must be continued as quickly as possible, especially in the regions most in need. Efforts are being made, and should be extended, to persuade people of the wisdom and necessity of limiting the size of families.

If such efforts should fail, and the population were to increase appreciably more than the food supply, the result would inevitably be disastrous. Assuming, more optimistically, that the supply of food will in future grow somewhat faster than the population does, there must still be limits beyond which population density cannot go. Simple lack of space would be the ultimate limit, but psychological factors would intervene at a much lower density. It is to be hoped that rational planning of our abundance will be achieved in time to avert a global population disaster.

This brief discussion has perhaps shown that the simple principles of population dynamics apply to human populations, but that economic, social and psychological factors also play an important part, to a much greater degree than organized behaviour patterns do among the social animals.

Exercises

Directions for a number of convenient practical exercises in population dynamics
are given by ANDREWARTHA (1961), LEWIS and TAYLOR (1967) and in the volume
edited by LAMBERT (1967). MacARTHUR and CONNELL (1966) describe several
relevant laboratory exercises.

The following are a few exercises for calculation. Like those in the text of some
earlier sections, some are much simplified versions of more realistic problems.
This is necessary for brevity. Their purpose is to illustrate points of general
significance. The numbers indicate the chapters to which they are relevant.

3a If an insect has equal numbers of males and females, and each female lays
on average 160 eggs, what rate of juvenile mortality would be required to prevent
an upward or downward drift of abundance?

What must the above mortality become if the sex ratio is 55 per cent females?

3b If a population were reduced to the same number each winter by a limited
food supply, increasing again 10-fold each spring, what percentage mortality
could be inflicted in the summer without reducing the numbers surviving to the
following spring? What could this summer mortality be if the spring increase were
(i) 5-fold or (ii) 50-fold?

3c Suppose that a population of animals suffers 50 per cent mortality as it
develops to maturity and that each surviving female lays 50 eggs all on the 20th
day of its life, half of them female. What would be its (multiplicative) rate of
increase per day, and per week? Compare the effects on the rate of increase of (a)
halving the mortality, (b) doubling the number of eggs, and (c) halving the
developmental period.

4a Here are three examples in which the numbers killed by a mortality factor
differ according to population density:

Density		50	100	200	500	1000
Deaths caused	case 1:	1	3	20	200	900
by mortality	case 2:	13	32	58	175	300
factor in	case 3:	15	29	40	70	80

Draw graphs to show how the percentages killed are related to density in each
case, and so identify the type of density-relationship involved.

Make up a further example of each of the three types of relationship.

4b On graph paper, make an approximate copy of Fig. 5–4, smoothing out
the minor fluctuations. Then plot numbers of predators against numbers of prey,
reading the values from your graph at half-monthly intervals along the time scale;
rule lines to link successive points.

5a Tabulate the classifications in §5.1, with two or three columns for each,
then write the examples given (or other examples), in a list on the left, and tick the
columns appropriate to each example.

5b   Suppose the graph line in Fig. 4–9 fell in position A, or in position B, what would be its biological interpretation? Write the equation for each line, also for the lines in Figs. 4–3 and 4–5.

6a   The data in Fig. 6–2 are as follows. Seeds sown per pot: 1, 5, 50, 100, 200. Seeds produced per plant that grew from the sown seeds and reproduced: 23 741; 6102; 990; 451; 210. Surface area of soil in pot 182.5 cm². The curve in Fig. 6–2 resembles a hyperbola, suggesting that the number of seeds per reproducing plant may be proportional to the space per plant. Test this by plotting seed production against the reciprocal of sowing density: do the points fall along a straight line?

6b   On page 48 two interpretations are given of the results of the experiments of WHITTINGTON and O'BRIEN. Are these interpretations mutually exclusive, or compatible?

7   From the data in Table 4, calculate the approximate mean rate of increase for each country at particular times. For example, using the U.K. figures for 1932, the difference between birth rate and death rate is $15.8 - 12.3 = 3.5$ per 1000, i.e. 0.35% increase per annum.

References

Books or papers marked * are recommended for general reading. Others deal with specific points referred to in the text or in the captions to illustrations or tables.

*ALLEE, W. C., EMERSON, A. E., PARK, O., PARK, T., and SCHMIDT, K. P. (1949). *Principles of Animal Ecology*. W. B. Saunders Co., Philadelphia and London.

*ANDREWARTHA, H. G. (1970). *Introduction to the Study of Animal Populations*. 2nd edn., Chapman & Hall, London.

*ANDREWARTHA, H. G. and BIRCH, L. C. (1954). *The Distribution and Abundance of Animals*. University of Chicago Press, Chicago.

ASPINALL, D. and MILTHORPE, F. L. (1959). *Ann. appl. Biol.*, **47**, 156–72.

BURGES, H. D. and HUSSEY, N. W. (Eds.) (1971). *Microbial Control of Insects and Mites*. Academic Press, London and New York.

BURNETT, T. (1958a). *Can. Ent.*, **90**, 279–83.

BURNETT, T. (1958b). *Proc. Xth Int. Congr. Entom.* (Montreal, 1956), **2**, 679–86.

CHAPMAN, R. N. (1931). *Animal Ecology, with Especial Reference to Insects*. McGraw-Hill, New York.

*CLARK, L. R., GEIER, P. W., HUGHES, R. D., and MORRIS, R. F. (1967). *The Ecology of Populations in Theory and Practice*. Methuen, London.

CLATWORTHY, J. N. and HARPER, J. L. (1962). *J. exper. Bot.*, **13**, 307–24.

*COLINVAUX, P. A. (1973). *Introduction to Ecology*. Wiley, New York, London and Sydney (Paperback).

*DeBACH, PAUL (Ed.) (1964). *Biological Control of Insect Pests and Weeds*. Chapman & Hall, London.

*DeBACH, PAUL (1974). *Biological Control by Natural Enemies*. Cambridge University Press, London.

DEMPSTER, J. P. (1975). *Animal Population Ecology*. Academic Press, London, New York, San Francisco.

DONALD, C. M. (1961). Pp. 282–313 in *Mechanisms in Biological Competition*. Edited by MILTHORPE, F. L. University Press, Cambridge.

DONALD, C. M. (1963). Competition among crop and pasture plants. *Advances in Agronomy*, **15**, 1–118. Academic Press, London and New York.

*EHRLICH, P. R. and EHRLICH, ANNE H. (1972). *Population, Resources, Environment* (2nd edn.). W. H. Freeman & Co., San Francisco.

*ELTON, CHARLES (1927; paperback edition 1966). *Animal Ecology*. Associated Book Publishers, London.

*ELTON, CHARLES S. (1958). *The Ecology of Invasions by Animals and Plants*. Methuen, London.

HAMMOND, J. (1955). Pp. 113–20 in *The Numbers of Man and Animals*. Edited by CRAGG, J. B. and PIRIE, N. W. Oliver and Boyd, Edinburgh and London.

*HARDY, SIR ALISTER (1959). *The Open Sea: Its Natural History, Part II, Fish and Fisheries*. Collins, London.

HARPER, J. L. (1960). Pp. 119–32 in *The Biology of Weeds*. Edited by HARPER, J. L. Blackwell, Oxford.

HARPER, J. L. and MCNAUGHTON, I. H. (1962). *New Phytol.*, **61**, 175–88.

HOLLING, C. S. (1959a). *Can. Ent.*, **91**, 293–320.

HOLLING, C. S. (1959b). *Can. Ent.*, **91**, 385–98.

HOLLING, C. S. (1963). *Mem. Entom. Soc. Canada*, No. **32**, 22–32.

HOLLING, C. S. (1964). *Can. Ent.*, **96**, 335–47.

*HUFFAKER, C. B. (Ed.) (1971). *Biological Control*. Plenum Press, New York and London.

HUSSEY, N. W. and BRAVENBOER, L. (1971). Pp. 195–216 in HUFFAKER (1971).

HUSSEY, N. W., PARR, W. J. and GOULD, H. J. (1965). *Ent. exp. appl.*, **8**, 271–81.

JONES, D. PRICE, and SOLOMON, M. E. (Eds.) (1974). *Biology in Pest and Disease Control.* Blackwell, Oxford.

*LACK, D. (1966). *Population Studies of Birds*. Clarendon Press, Oxford.

LAMBERT, J. M. (Ed.) (1967). *The Teaching of Ecology*. Blackwell, Oxford and Edinburgh.

*LEWIS, T. and TAYLOR, L. R. (1967). *Introduction to Experimental Ecology*. Academic Press, London and New York.

*MacARTHUR, R. and CONNELL, J. (1966). *The Biology of Populations*. Wiley, New York, London and Sydney.

*MACFADYEN, A. (1963). *Animal Ecology. Aims and Methods*. Pitman, London.

MCLAREN, I. A. (1971). *Natural Regulation of Animal Populations*. Atherton Press, New York.

MILTHORPE, F. L. (1961). Pp. 330–55 in *Mechanisms in Biological Competition*. Edited by MILTHORPE, F. L. University Press, Cambridge.

MORRIS, R. F. (1957). *Can. Ent.*, **89**, 49–69.

MORRIS, R. F. (1963). *Mem. Entom. Soc. Canada*, No. **32**, 16–21.

NEWTON, I. (1967). *J. Anim. Ecol.*, **36**, 721–44. Also (1972) *Finches*. New Naturalist Series. Collins, London.

*NICHOLSON, A. J. (1954). *Aust. J. Zool.*, **2**, 9–65.

NICHOLSON, A. J. and BAILEY, V. A. (1935). *Proc. zool. Soc. Lond.*, **3**, 551–98.

ODUM, E. P. (1959). *Fundamentals of Ecology*. Saunders, Philadelphia and London.

PALMBLAD, I. G. (1968). *Ecology*, **49**, 26–34.

*PARK, T. (1955). Pp. 69–84 in *The Numbers of Man and Animals*. Edited by CRAGG, J. B. and PIRIE, N. W. Oliver and Boyd, Edinburgh and London.

PARK, T. (1962). *Science, N.Y.* **138**, 1369–75.

*PHILLIPSON, J. (1966). *Ecological Energetics*. Arnold, London.

*RICHARDS, O. W. (1958). The study of natural populations of insects. *Proc. R. Ent. Soc. Lond.*, Ser. C., **23**, 75–9.

SAGAR, G. R. and HARPER, J. L. (1961). *Weed Res.*, **1**, 163–76.

SOLOMON, M. E. (1962). *Ann. appl. Biol.* **50**, 178–84.

SOLOMON, M. E. (1973), *Scient. Hort.* **24**, 181–90.

*SOUTHWOOD, T. R. E. (1966). *Ecological Methods*. Methuen, London.

*SOUTHWOOD, T. R. E. (Ed.) (1968). *Insect Abundance*. Blackwell, Oxford and Edinburgh.

VARLEY, G. C. and GRADWELL, G. R. (1968). Pp. 132–42 in *Insect Abundance*. Edited by SOUTHWOOD, T. R. E. Blackwell, Oxford and Edinburgh.

*VARLEY, G. C., GRADWELL, G. R. and HASSELL, M. P. (1973). *Insect Population Ecology*. Blackwell, Oxford.

*WATERHOUSE, D. F. and WILSON, FRANK (1968). *Science Journal*, **4**, 31–7.

WATT, A. S. (1955). *J. Ecol.*, **43**, 490–506.

WHITTINGTON, W. J. and O'BRIEN, T. A. (1968). *J. appl. Ecol.*, 5, 209–13.

WILLIAMSON, M. H. (1967). Pp. 169–76 in *The Teaching of Ecology*. Edited by LAMBERT, J. M. Blackwell, Oxford and Edinburgh.

WILLIAMSON, MARK (1972). *The Analysis of Biological Populations*. Edward Arnold, London.

WYATT, I. J. (1974). Pp. 294–301 in JONES and SOLOMON (1974).

WYNNE-EDWARDS, V. C. (1962). *Animal Dispersion in Relation to Social Behaviour*. Oliver and Boyd, Edinburgh and London.